The Elements and their Order

CYRIL PARSONS, B.Sc. CLARE DOVER, B.Sc.

FOUNDATIONS OF SCIENCE LIBRARY

GREYSTONE PRESS/NEW YORK · TORONTO · LONDON

This new presentation assembles freshly edited material from 'Understanding Science' on one subject into a single volume.

Library of Congress Catalog Card Number: 66–17993

Printed in Great Britain
Manufactured in U.S.A.

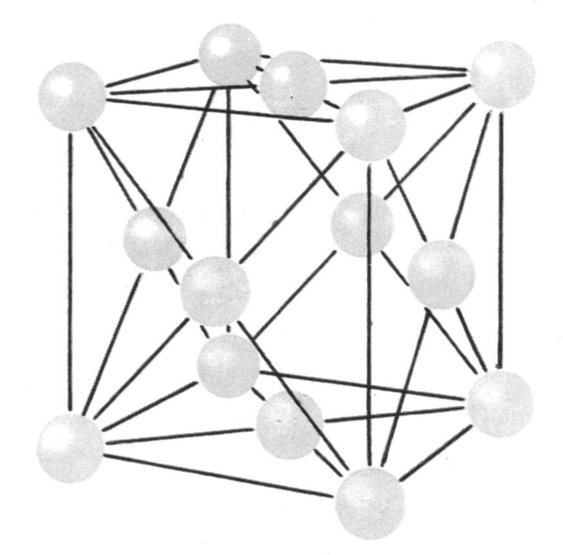

Contents

An Introduction to the Periodic Table

CHAPTER ONE

Arranging the Elements

Early History

One of the main purposes of all science is to arrange in a systematic manner information which has been collected by careful experiment and patient observation of the materials and living organisms of the Universe. The system by which the chemical elements are now classified has been thoroughly justified following investigations within the past 60 years into the atomic structure of the various elements. However, Mendeleef, Newlands and Lothar Meyer had no such information to guide them when they set about classifying the elements 100 years ago. The only basis upon which they could build a classification was the known chemical properties of the elements themselves, and it is a mark of their brilliance and a credit to the accuracy of their observations and experiments that the final classification was so accurate.

The expression 'properties of an element' embraces many aspects of its behaviour – whether it is a metal or non-metal, its resistance to attack by acids and alkalis, the elements with which it will join to form chemical compounds, and the nature of these compounds. Thus sodium and potassium are said to have similar chemical properties: both are reactive metals of low density which form similar crystalline salts with chlorine and other halogens.

In the early years of the nineteenth century some form of classification of the chemical elements began to emerge. In 1800 only 33 chemical elements had been isolated, but during the next 60 years this total was almost doubled. With the discovery of more elements it became obvious that some of them, notably the alkali metals (lithium, sodium and potassium) and the halogens (fluorine, chlorine, bromine and iodine) were in some way related since the elements in each group have similar properties. However, such a classification did not accommodate all the elements. This was partly because certain members of some of the families had not been isolated and also because in some groups the resemblance between individuals is only slight.

There was, therefore, a need for a more positive means of classification, perhaps based on measurements which would yield numerical values. The discovery and development of new materials during the nineteenth century contributed to better scientific apparatus and made possible more accurate experimental results. Thus, before the introduction of rubber tubing in the 1840's connections between pieces of apparatus could only be made with glass, pottery, metal or fibres. As a consequence, joints tended to leak, and results were unreliable.

As such improved apparatus and more accurate instruments became available, chemists and workers in other branches of science as well were not only able to extend their studies but also able to consolidate previous knowledge by repeating measurements in an attempt to obtain more accurate and reliable results.

It was against this background that S. Cannizzaro, J. B. A. Dumas, J. S. Stas and others set out in the 1850's to determine afresh the *atomic weights* of the known elements. The atomic weight of an element is the number of times one atom of it is heavier than an atom of hydrogen. (The standard upon which atomic weights are based has since been modified. All measurements are now related to the atomic weight of carbon isotope 12 as exactly 12 mass units.)

While studying the revised value for the atomic weights, John Newlands, a British industrial chemist, realized that there was some correlation between atomic weights and the chemical properties of the elements. In 1865 he arranged the known elements in ascending order of their atomic weights and noticed that 'the eighth element, starting from the given one, is a kind of repetition of the first'. Thus in his table fluorine is No. 8, chlorine No. 15 and bromine No. 29. Newlands likened this repetition to the octaves of the musical scale, and his deduction relating to the periodic repetition of similar elements became known as the *law of octaves*.

In 1869 the Russian chemist Dmitri Ivanovich Mendeleef and Julius Lothar Meyer, a German, published somewhat similar Periodic Tables independently. They arranged the elements according to their atomic weights, in much the same way as Newlands had done, but both of them had the foresight to recognise the possibility of there being further elements still to discover. Accordingly they left gaps in the table for unknown elements, and in this way were able to accommodate elements with similar properties in the same column. The form of Mendeleef's table of 1869 has been followed closely in the modern table. The elements were arranged in short sequences with similar ones underneath each other.

Not only did Mendeleef leave gaps in the table for new elements. He also deduced their more important properties from the properties of adjacent elements in the table. As is often the case with new ideas, chemists were at first sceptical of this classification. Their attitude changed when the element gallium was discovered in 1875 and was found to have the properties which Mendeleef had predicted.

Simplified Periodic Table

The *law of octaves* indicated that if elements are arranged in order of their atomic weights, each element (with certain exceptions which will be discussed later) resembles other elements in the Table eight places and a multiple of eight places removed from itself. In the simplified version of the Periodic Table shown overleaf, these similar elements are arranged in groups, or families. It can be seen that the elements which make up each family all have the same number of electrons in their outer shells.

All the chemical properties (and many of the physical properties) of the elements are decided by the arrangements of the electrons in the shells. The outer shell is particularly

First Family of Elements (each with only ONE electron in the outer shell)

HYDROGEN no. 1 element has 1 proton

LITHIUM no. 3 element has 3 protons

SODIUM no. 11 element has 11 protons

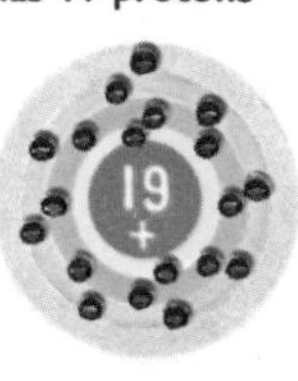

POTASSIUM no. 19 element has 19 protons

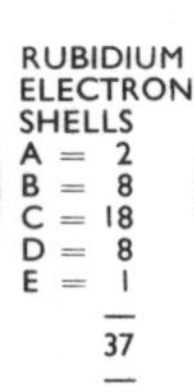

RUBIDIUM no. 37 element has 37 protons

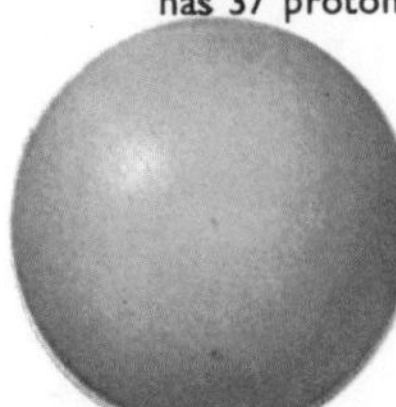
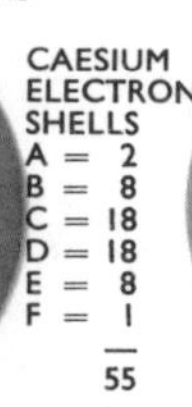

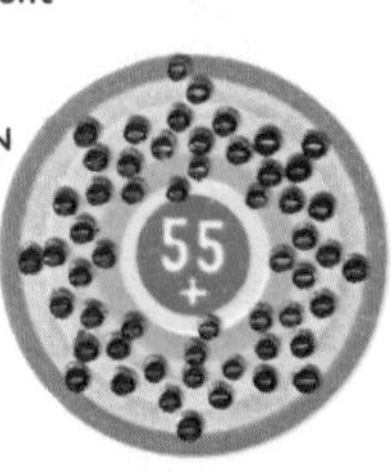

CAESIUM no. 55 element has 55 protons

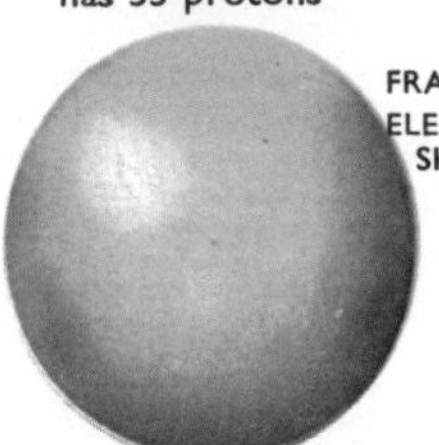
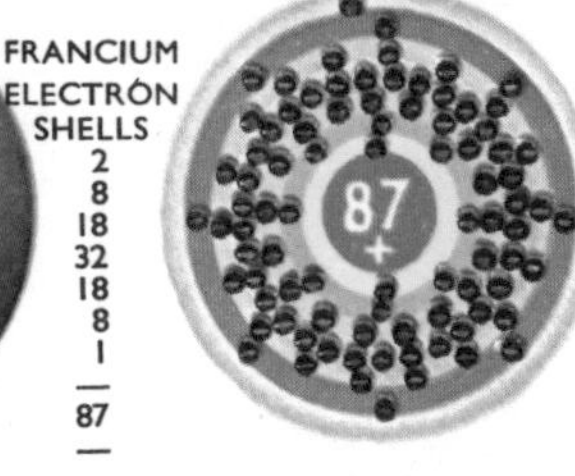

FRANCIUM no. 87 element has 87 protons

Second Family of Elements (each with TWO electrons in outer shell)

BERYLLIUM no. 4 element has 4 protons

MAGNESIUM no. 12 element has 12 protons

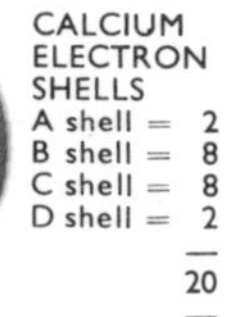

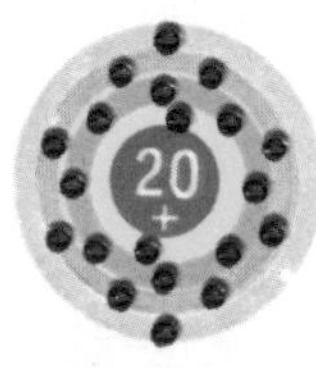

CALCIUM no. 20 element has 20 protons

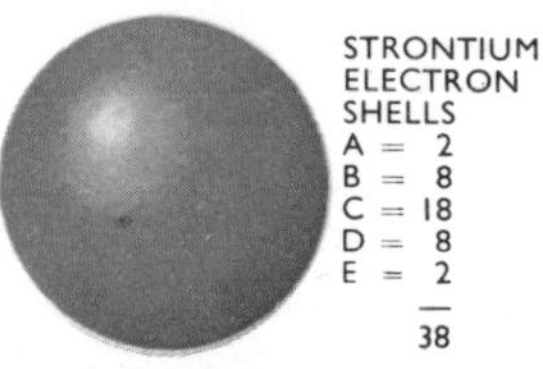

STRONTIUM no. 38 element has 38 protons

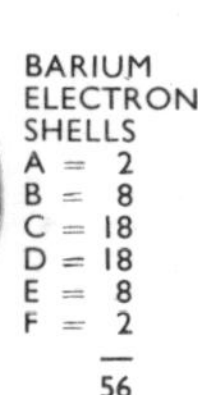

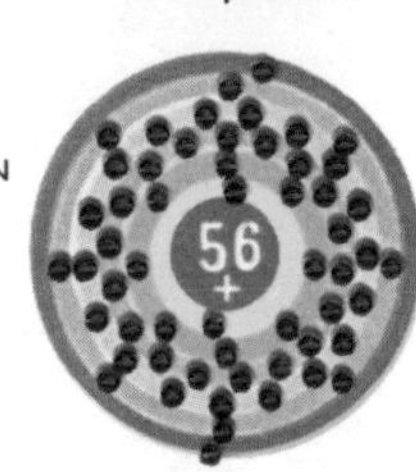

BARIUM no. 56 element has 56 protons

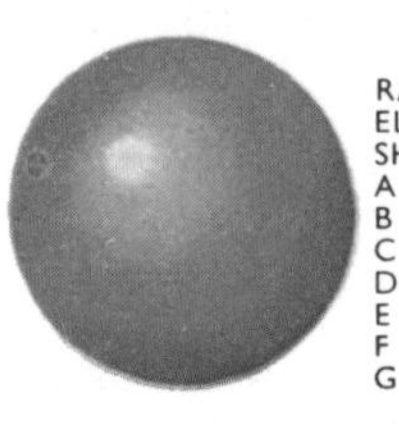
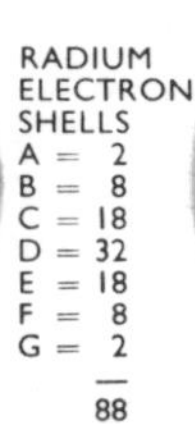

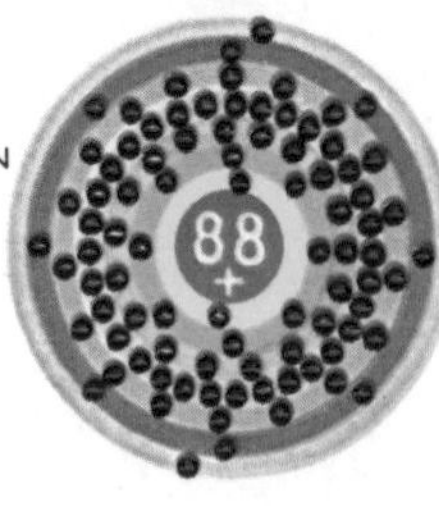

RADIUM no. 88 element has 88 protons

Third Family of Elements (each with THREE electrons in outer shell)

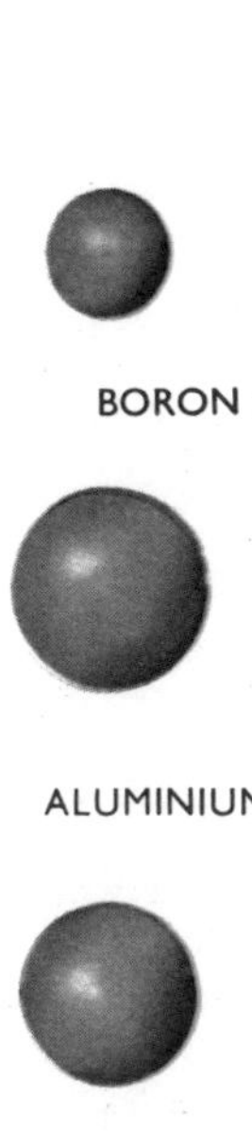
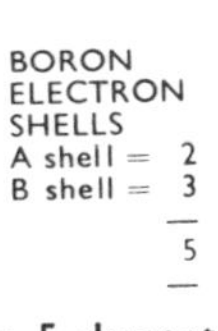

BORON no. 5 element has 5 protons

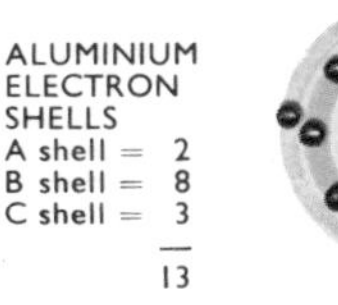

ALUMINIUM no. 13 element has 13 protons

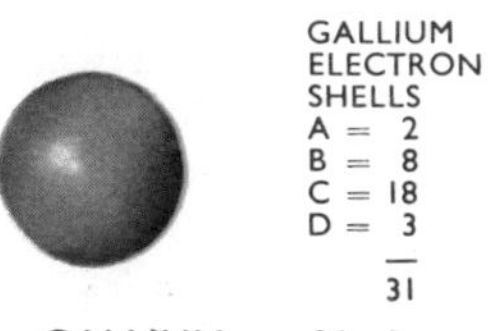

GALLIUM no. 31 element has 31 protons

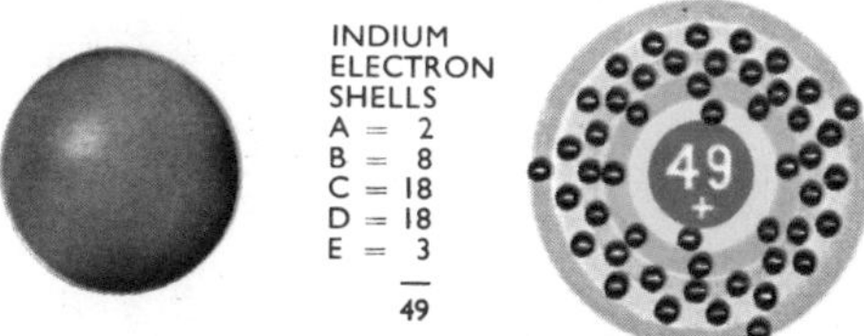

INDIUM no. 49 element has 49 protons

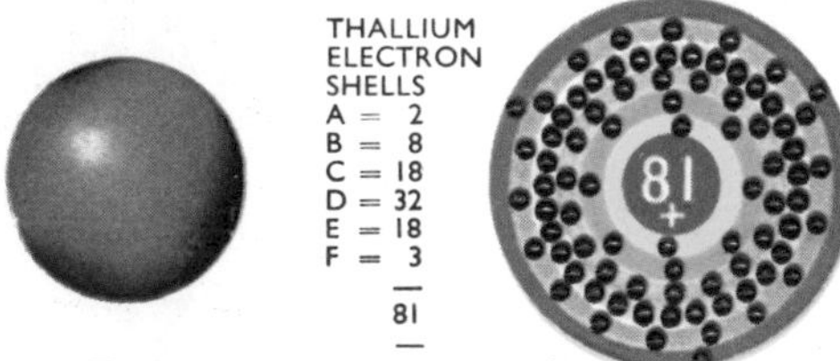

THALLIUM no. 81 element has 81 protons

Fourth Family of Elements (each with FOUR electrons in outer shell)

CARBON
ELECTRON
SHELLS
A shell = 2
B shell = 4
6

CARBON no. 6 element has 6 protons

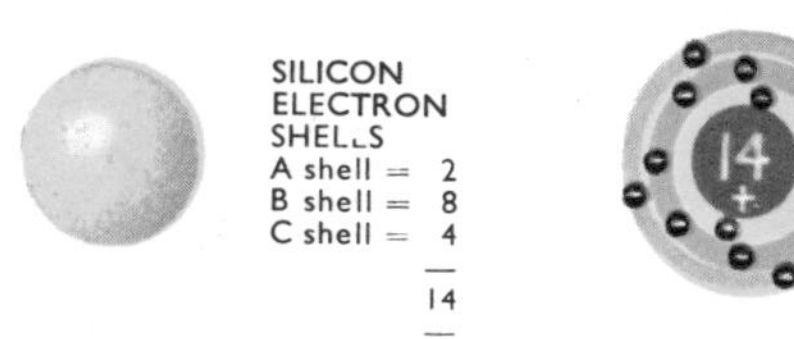

SILICON no. 14 element has 14 protons

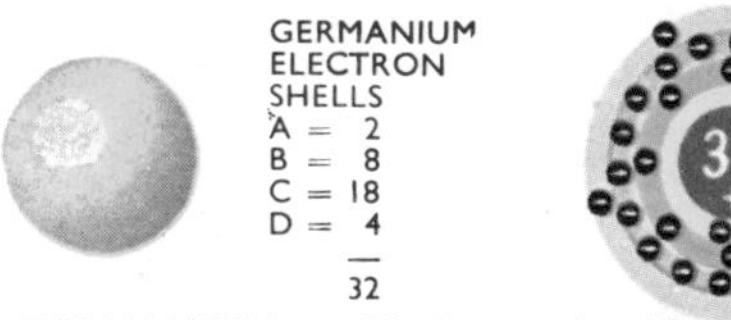

GERMANIUM no. 32 element has 32 protons

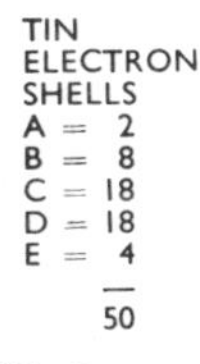
TIN
ELECTRON
SHELLS
A = 2
B = 8
C = 18
D = 18
E = 4
50

TIN no. 50 element has 50 protons

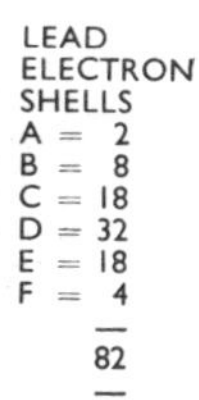
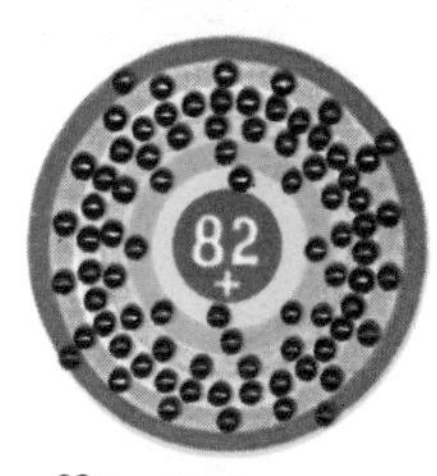

LEAD no. 82 element has 82 protons

important because it contains the *valence electrons*. These are the electrons that can be given to other atoms to form *electrovalent* bonds, or shared with other atoms in *covalent* bonds. The number of electrons in the outer shell is the main factor that decides what sorts of chemical reactions the element undergoes and how it becomes bonded to other atoms. So, by arranging the elements in the periodic classification, based on their chemical properties. Mendeleeff automatically sorted the elements into *groups* with equal numbers of 'outer shell' electrons.

However, there are many exceptions to the *law of octaves*. Looking at the first family we see that Lithium, Sodium and Potassium do indeed comply with the law, since Sodium

Fifth Family of Elements (each with FIVE electrons in outer shell)

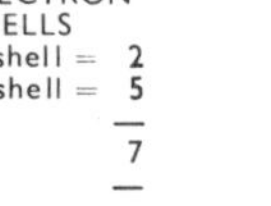

NITROGEN
ELECTRON
SHELLS
A shell = 2
B shell = 5
7

NITROGEN no 7 element has 7 protons

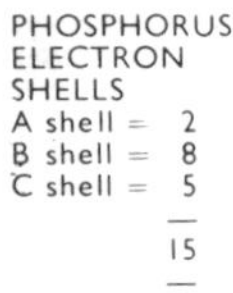

PHOSPHORUS
ELECTRON
SHELLS
A shell = 2
B shell = 8
C shell = 5
15

PHOSPHORUS no. 15 element has 15 protons

ARSENIC
ELECTRON
SHELLS
A shell = 2
B shell = 8
C shell = 18
D shell = 5
33

ARSENIC no. 33 element has 33 protons

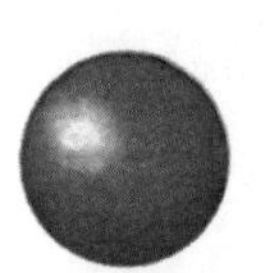

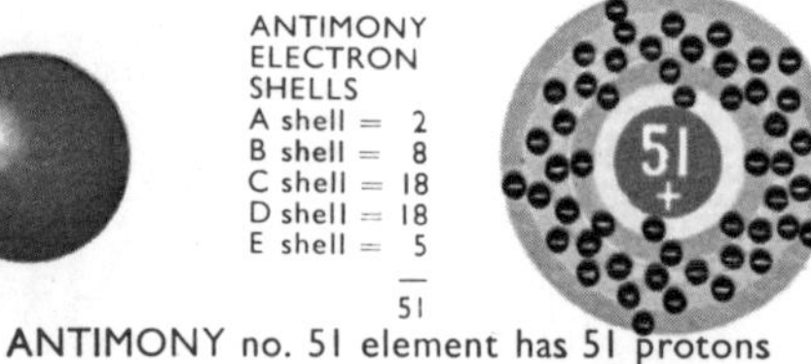

ANTIMONY
ELECTRON
SHELLS
A shell = 2
B shell = 8
C shell = 18
D shell = 18
E shell = 5
51

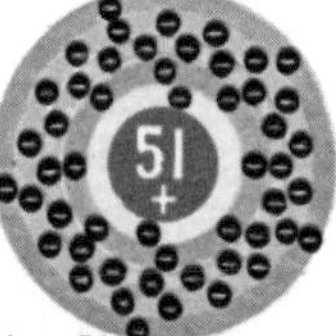

ANTIMONY no. 51 element has 51 protons

BISMUTH
ELECTRON
SHELLS
A shell = 2
B shell = 8
C shell = 18
D shell = 32
E shell = 18
F shell = 5
83

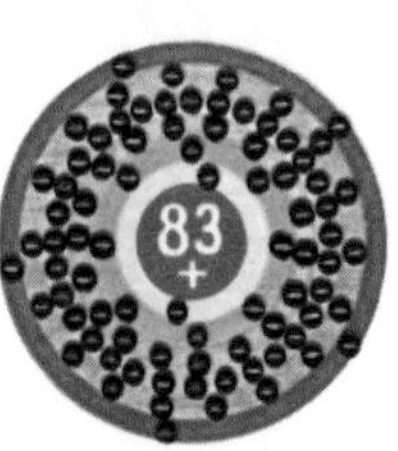

BISMUTH no. 83 element has 83 protons

Sixth Family of Elements (each with SIX electrons in outer shell)

OXYGEN
ELECTRON
SHELLS
A shell = 2
B shell = 6
8

OXYGEN no. 8 element has 8 protons

SULPHUR
ELECTRON
SHELLS
A shell = 2
B shell = 8
C shell = 6
16

SULPHUR no. 16 element has 16 protons

SELENIUM
ELECTRON
SHELLS
A shell = 2
B shell = 8
C shell = 18
D shell = 6
34

SELENIUM no. 34 element has 34 protons

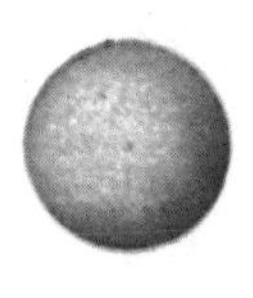

TELLURIUM
ELECTRON
SHELLS
A shell = 2
B shell = 8
C shell = 18
D shell = 18
E shell = 6
52

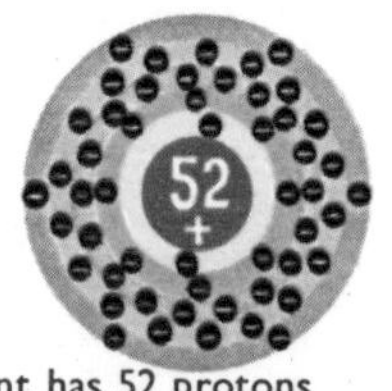

TELLURIUM no. 52 element has 52 protons

POLONIUM
ELECTRON
SHELLS
A shell = 2
B shell = 8
C shell = 18
D shell = 32
E shell = 18
F shell = 6
84

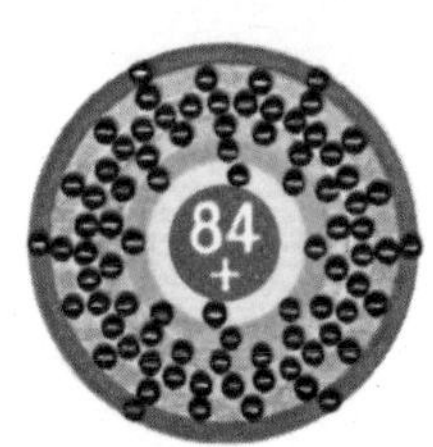

POLONIUM no. 84 element has 84 protons

Atomic Structure

Every atom has at its centre a core or nucleus. This nucleus is made up of particles of two sorts. Some are *Protons*: these have a positive electrical charge. Some are *Neutrons*: these have no electrical charge, they are neutral.

Around the nucleus and at some distance from it fly some much smaller particles. These are *Electrons*: each one has a negative electrical charge which exactly balances the positive charge on one proton in the nucleus. As every atom normally has exactly the same number of protons and electrons, the atom is held in balance. The electron orbits in every atom are arranged in a series of shells. The innermost shell can hold no more than two electrons and the second shell can hold no more than eight. The heavier atoms have more shells.

NOTE. In advanced text-books (and elsewhere in this book) the electron shells are labelled K, L, M, N, etc., instead of A, B, C, D, etc. The reasons for this are largely historical.

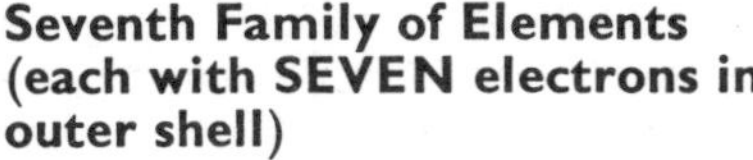

Seventh Family of Elements (each with SEVEN electrons in outer shell)

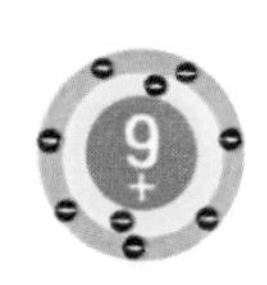

FLUORINE
ELECTRON
SHELLS
A shell = 2
B shell = 7
9

FLUORINE no. 9 element has 9 protons

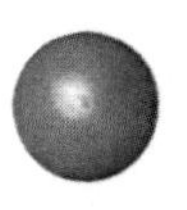

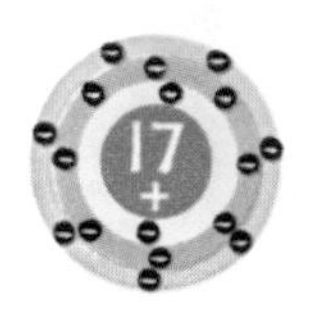

CHLORINE
ELECTRON
SHELLS
A shell = 2
B shell = 8
C shell = 7
17

CHLORINE no. 17 element has 17 protons

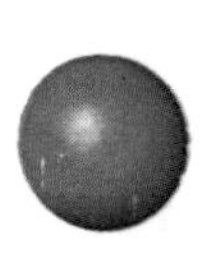

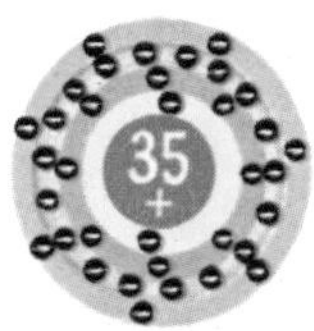

BROMINE
ELECTRON
SHELLS
A shell = 2
B shell = 8
C shell = 18
D shell = 7
35

BROMINE no. 35 element has 35 protons

IODINE
ELECTRON
SHELLS
A shell = 2
B shell = 8
C shell = 18
D shell = 18
E shell = 7
53

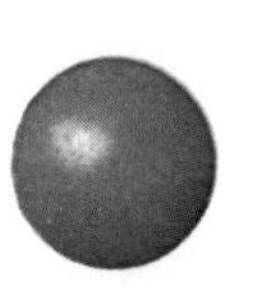

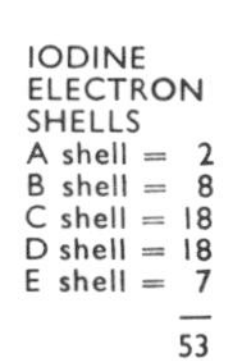

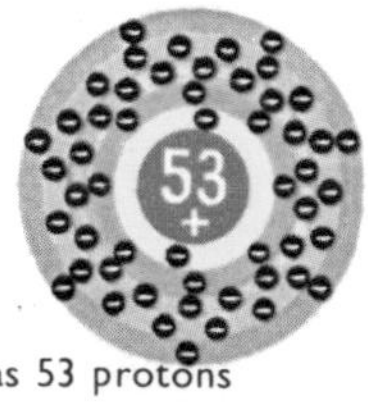

IODINE no. 53 element has 53 protons

ASTATINE
ELECTRON
SHELLS
A shell = 2
B shell = 8
C shell = 18
D shell = 32
E shell = 18
F shell = 7
85

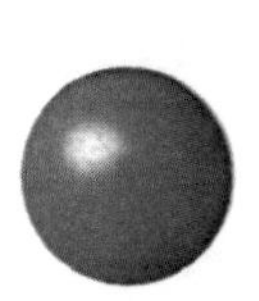

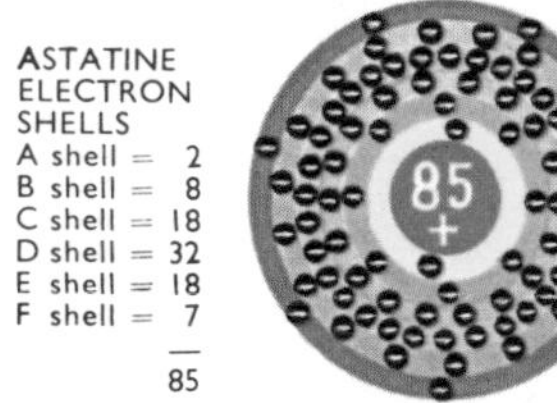

ASTATINE no. 85 element has 85 protons

Eighth Family of Elements (each with a complete outer shell of EIGHT electrons)

HELIUM
ELECTRON SHELLS
A shell = 2 electrons

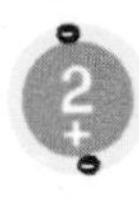

HELIUM no. 2 element has 2 protons

NEON
ELECTRON
SHELLS
A shell = 2 electrons
B shell = 8 electrons
10

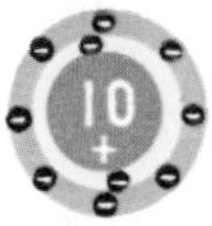

NEON no. 10 element has 10 protons

ARGON
ELECTRON
SHELLS
A shell = 2
B shell = 8
C shell = 8
18

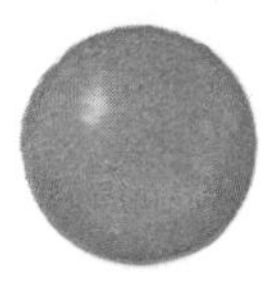

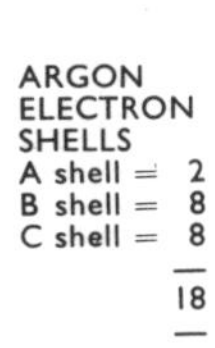

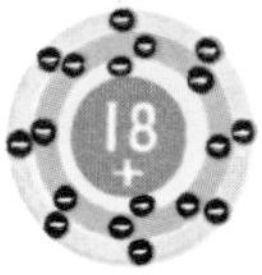

ARGON no. 18 element has 18 protons

KRYPTON
ELECTRON
SHELLS
A shell = 2
B shell = 8
C shell = 18
D shell = 8
36

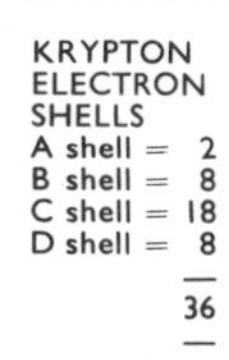

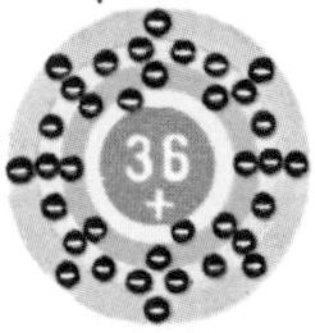

KRYPTON no. 36 element has 36 protons

XENON
ELECTRON
SHELLS
A = 2
B = 8
C = 18
D = 18
E = 8
54

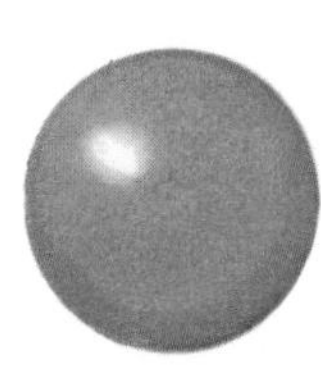

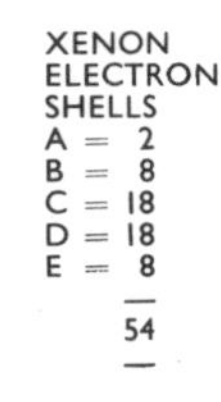

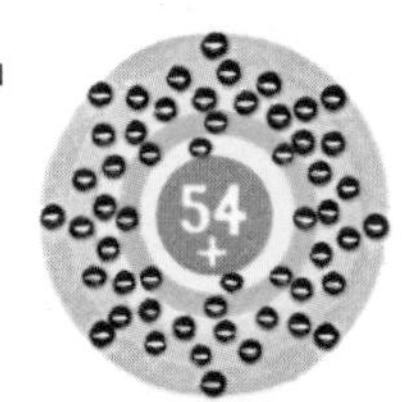

XENON no. 54 element has 54 protons

RADON
ELECTRON
SHELLS
A = 2
B = 8
C = 18
D = 32
E = 18
F = 8
86

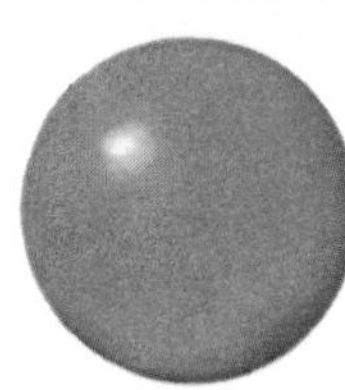

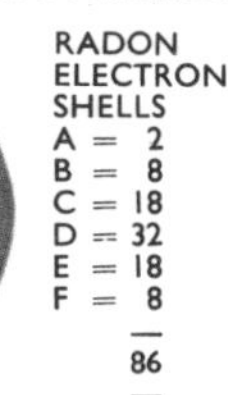

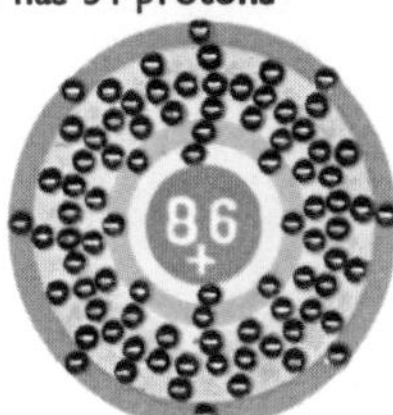

RADON no. 86 element has 86 protons

Suggestions for Scanning this Simplified Chart of Elements

Reading across from left to right: The elements appear in their order of rank, although not all the elements are shown. The number of protons in the nucleus is the Atomic Number of the element. Each element can be checked to ascertain that these positively charged protons are balanced by an equal number of negatively charged electrons.

Reading downwards in columns: Each element in a 'family' has the same number of electrons in its outermost shell.

has an atomic number eight higher than Lithium, and Potassium in turn is eight places higher than Sodium. On the other hand Potassium – Rubidium – Caesium – Francium are certainly not eight places removed from each other. The reason for this departure from the law may be seen if the Table is considered horizontally: the elements are all present from 1–20 but elements 21–30 inclusive are missing, as are elements 39–48, 57–80 and 89–103. If these 'misfit' elements did not exist and the remainder of the elements were numbered consecutively, the law of octaves would be correct almost without exception. For instance Gallium would be numbered 21 instead of 31, which would grant it an atomic number eight away from Aluminium (vertically above Gallium in Family number three).

Knowing as we do that the composition of the shells of electrons orbiting the nucleus has accounted for the groupings of the elements in the Table, we would be correct in suspecting that the electron build-up in these 'misfit' elements differs from the normal pattern.

What is the normal pattern? The answer to this question can be seen from a closer examination of the Table. Note that as the *Atomic Number* increases from 1 to 20, so does the total number of electrons in the shells; thus Calcium (Number 20) has one more electron in Shell D than Potassium (Number 19). Note also that each shell does not accommodate the same number of electrons before it is 'full up'.

Returning to the problem of the 'misfit' electrons, the element we would expect to follow Calcium should contain one extra electron in Shell D, i.e. Shell D should contain three electrons. In fact Gallium *does* have three electrons in Shell D, but it also has an additional *ten* electrons in Shell C! This supplies the missing clue, because it is now apparent that elements 21–30 have been filling up

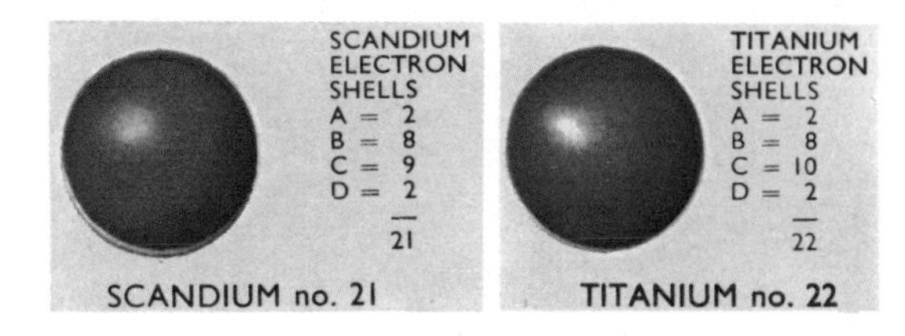

SCANDIUM no. 21 TITANIUM no. 22

their C shell with further electrons before adding to their outer D shell.

This is confusing because normally electrons 'fill up' their shells before progressing on to a new one, but in the case of Potassium and Calcium this did not happen.

Similar circumstances arise in the case of elements 39–48, 57–80 and 89–103.

The Complete Periodic Table

The entire Periodic Table, now shown, once again presents the elements in their order of rank. In order to allow the elements to remain in their families, the 'misfit' elements have been depicted separately, but at the same time their position in the Table is clearly shown.

Elements 21–30, 39–48, 72–80 are known as the *Transition Elements* and are covered fully in Chapter Six.

Elements 57–71 are called the *Rare Earths*, while 89–103 are named the *Actinide Series* of Elements. Numbers 93–103 are artificially-made elements. (See illustrations on pages 14 and 15.)

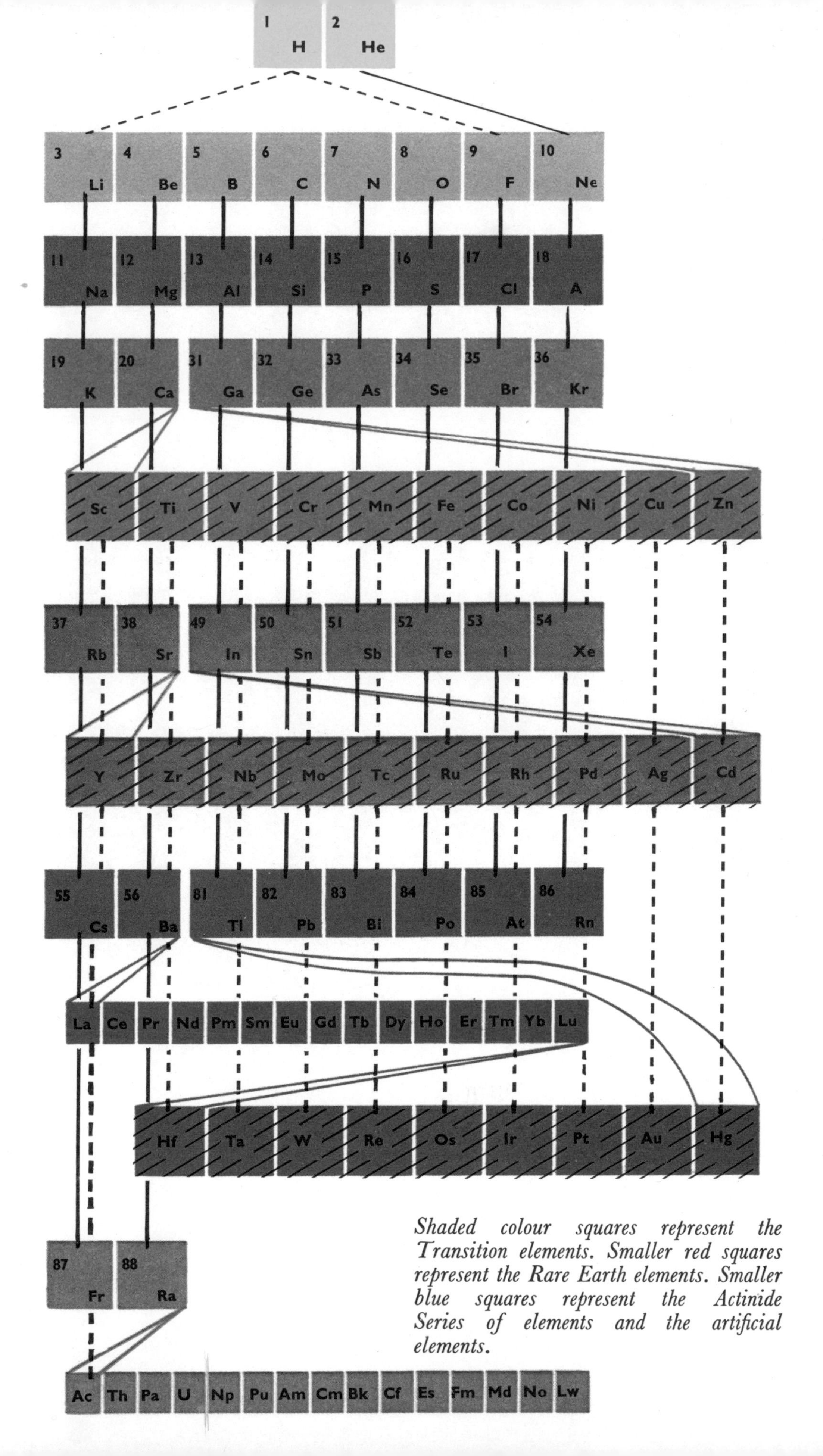

Shaded colour squares represent the Transition elements. Smaller red squares represent the Rare Earth elements. Smaller blue squares represent the Actinide Series of elements and the artificial elements.

THE RARE EARTHS
Electron shell D changes

No. 57 LANTHANUM
Electron shells:
A = 2; B = 8; C = 18;
D = 18; E = 9; F = 2.
Total 57.

No. 58 CERIUM
Electron shells:
A = 2; B = 8; C = 18;
D = 20; E = 8; F = 2.
Total 58.

No. 59 PRASEODYMIUM
Electron shells:
A = 2; B = 8; C = 18;
D = 21; E = 8; F = 2.
Total 59.

No. 60 NEODYMIUM
Electron shells:
A= 2; B=8; C=18;
D=22; E=8; F= 2;
Total 60

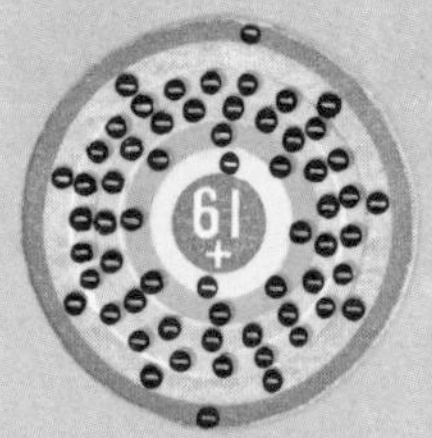

No. 61 PROMETHIUM
Electron shells:
A = 2; B = 8; C = 18;
D = 23; E = 8; F = 2.
Total 61.

No. 62 SAMARIUM
Electron Shells
A = 2; B = 8; C = 18;
D = 24; E = 8; F = 2.
Total 62.

No. 63 EUROPIUM
Electron shells:
A = 2; B = 8; C = 18;
D = 25; E = 8; F = 2.
Total 63.

No. 64 GADOLINIUM
Electron shells:
A = 2; B = 8; C = 18;
D = 25; E = 9; F = 2.
Total 64.

No. 65 TERBIUM
Electron shells:
A = 2; B = 8; C = 18;
D = 27; E = 8; F = 2.
Total 65.

No. 66 DYSPROSIUM
Electron shells:
A= 2; B=8; C=18;
D=28; E=8; F= 2;
Total 66

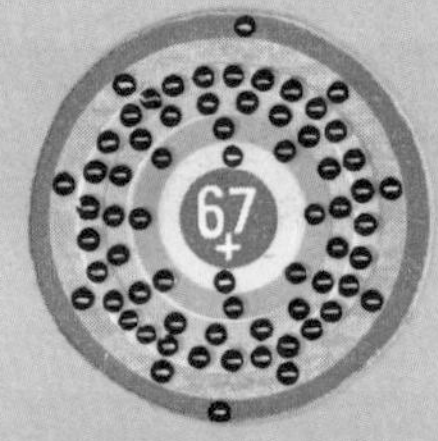

No. 67 HOLMIUM
Electron shells:
A = 2; B = 8; C = 18;
D = 29; E = 8; F = 2.
Total 67.

No. 68 ERBIUM
Electron shells:
A = 2; B = 8; C = 18;
D = 30; E = 8; F = 2.
Total 68.

No. 69 THULIUM
Electron shells:
A = 2; B = 8; C = 18;
D = 31; E = 8; F = 2.
Total 69.

No. 70 YTTERBIUM
Electron shells:
A = 2; B = 8; C = 18;
D = 32; E = 8; F = 2.
Total 70.

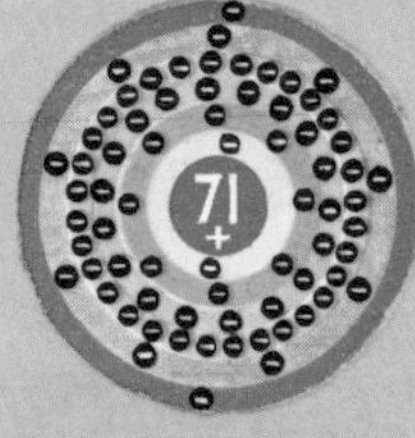

No. 71 LUTETIUM
Electron shells:
A = 2; B = 8; C = 18;
D = 32; E = 9; F = 2.
Total 71.

The 15 elements from lanthanum to lutetium are the rare earth elements.

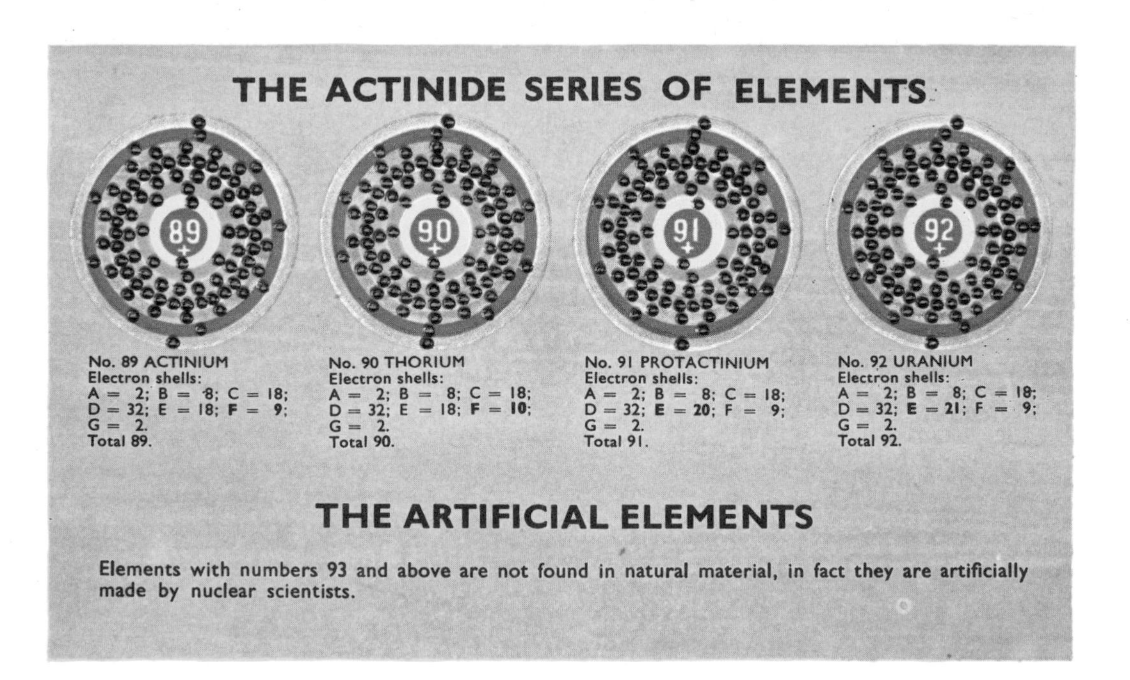

Advantages of Classification

Classifying the elements into the Periodic Table, according to the chemical properties which they display, has brought order to a vast array of elements and the seemingly unconnected reactions between these elements. Those elements which fall conveniently into 'families' enable us to observe the similarity of properties which not only they but also their derivatives display. Even the 'misfit' elements form groups which have their own characteristic behaviour patterns.

The following chapters discuss in some detail most of the important elements, supplementing the knowledge thus far gained about the Periodic Table by emphasising the very real similarities displayed by the elements in their respective 'families', and the role played by the Transition Elements.

CHAPTER TWO

The Elements of Life

Oxygen and Oxides

Oxygen and hydrogen do not occur in the same family, but they are such vitally important elements that they serve as a very useful introduction to the elements.

Oxygen is the most abundant and widespread of all the elements in Nature. Twenty-three parts (by weight) in every hundred of the air around us are pure oxygen. Eighty-nine parts (by weight) in every hundred of water consist of oxygen, but this oxygen is not free—it is chemically combined with another element called hydrogen. A simple combination of oxygen with another element is known as an *oxide*. Water is an oxide of hydrogen. It is of course a liquid whereas both oxygen and hydrogen are normally gases. Some oxides are gases, some are liquids and some are solids. Solid oxides make up most of the Earth's crust, and a great many metals are dug out of the ground in the form of ores that are solid oxides. Only a few oxides will release their oxygen when they are heated. Water for example, simply turns to steam on being heated. But an electric current passed through water, with a small amount of acid added to make it a better conductor, splits it into oxygen and hydrogen gases.

Oxygen gas is colourless and tasteless and has no odour. If the gas is shaken up with water a small amount of it is absorbed. The fact that it is absorbed at all is essential to the animals which live in water. Oxygen itself does not burn: burning is the combination of other substances with oxygen. At high temperatures oxygen is very reactive and combines with a very wide range of substances. When oxygen combines with a fuel energy is

Animals take in oxygen from the air and breathe out carbon dioxide. Burning also converts oxygen into carbon dioxide. But the amount of oxygen in the atmosphere remains constant because green plants take in carbon dioxide and release oxygen. Roughly one part in five of the air by volume, or twenty-three parts in a hundred by weight, is oxygen, the rest is almost all nitrogen.

Eighty-nine parts in a hundred by weight of water are oxygen, the rest is hydrogen. The two substances are chemically joined and cannot easily be separated. Water is called an oxide of hydrogen. It also contains dissolved *oxygen gas and it is this which fishes breathe.*

released in the form of heat and helps to maintain the reaction and to speed it up. A fuel burning in air combines with the oxygen in the air. The nitrogen (which forms almost the whole of the remaining four-fifths of the air) does not take part in the reaction. It merely dilutes the oxygen and slows down the burning. Substances burn much more fiercely in pure oxygen than they do in air. A piece of steel (iron) wool heated to redness does not burn in air. If the red-hot steel wool is plunged into a jar of oxygen it immediately bursts into flames. At normal temperatures iron slowly rusts. Rusting differs from burning, as it cannot take place without water being present. It is the slow combination of iron with oxygen and water.

Animals depend on oxygen because they get their energy from the chemical reaction of the food they eat with the oxygen they breathe. The food is first converted into glucose sugar and this reacts with oxygen to form water, carbon dioxide, and energy. Most fuels produce water, carbon dioxide and energy when they burn. Fortunately green plants take in carbon dioxide, and release oxygen, otherwise the world's supply of oxygen would become smaller every time we breathed, lit a fire, started a car, or fired a gun.

A jet plane gets its energy by burning fuel in air. It cannot fly where there is no air since the oxygen in the air is essential to burning. A rocket, on the other hand, can go above the atmosphere where there is

About a half (by weight) of the Earth's crust is oxygen locked up in solid oxides. Some of the solid oxides form the ores of important metals such as tin. Here tin ore is being hosed out. ▶

A piece of red-hot steel-wool plunged into a jar of oxygen bursts into flames. Oxygen is essential to burning. Substances which burn slowly in air (where the oxygen is diluted with nitrogen) burn fiercely in pure oxygen.

no air because as well as fuel it carries its own supply of oxygen with it. This may be either liquid oxygen or some chemical such as nitric acid that is rich in oxygen.

In industry, oxygen is chiefly used in steelmaking, where the impurities are burned out of molten iron by a blast of pure oxygen. It is used in welding, mixed with acetylene, to give a very hot flame. It is also very important in hospitals and to doctors.

Oxygen is manufactured from the air around us. Air is a *mixture* of gases—the oxygen and the nitrogen are not joined to each other. Liquid air is produced by cooling dust-free, dry air, to about 200°C below the freezing point of water, under pressure. It is a mixture of liquid gases, mainly nitrogen and oxygen. When liquid air slowly evaporates, nitrogen becomes gas first. The liquid remaining is almost pure oxygen. This is piped off into gigantic vacuum flasks, for it will remain liquid only as long as it can be kept cold. Oxygen is generally transported in the liquid form as this takes up far less space than the gas.

Oxygen can be prepared in the laboratory by heating a compound which is rich in oxygen, such as potassium permanganate. An excellent method is to drop hydrogen peroxide solution on to manganese dioxide, a substance which speeds up the release of oxygen from the peroxide without itself being used up. It is, however, most easily obtained from a cylinder.

Ozone

Normally the smallest particles (molecules) in a sample of oxygen gas consist of pairs of oxygen atoms merged together. *Ozone* is a different form of oxygen in which each molecule consists of three oxygen atoms merged together. Ozone is a pale blue gas and has a strong odour. It is used to sterilize water, to prevent bacterial growth in food stores, and in the manufacture of drugs and plasticizing materials.

The ozone molecule is a high-energy

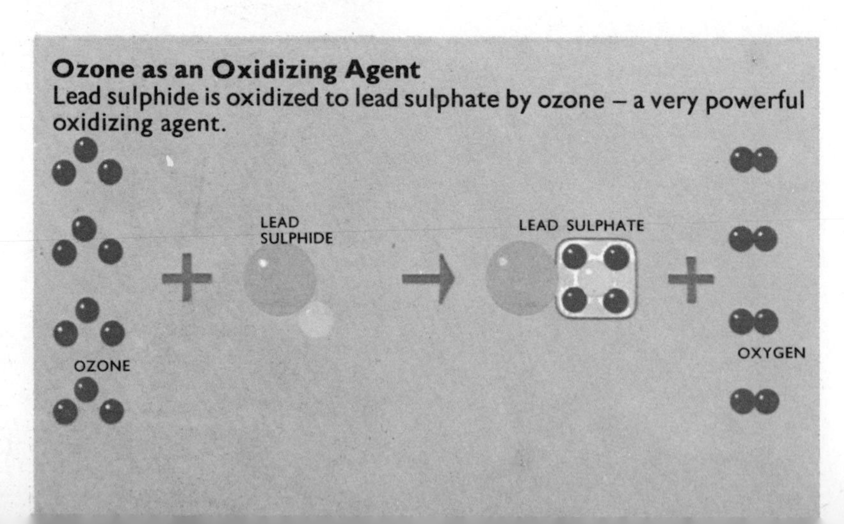

Ozone as an Oxidizing Agent
Lead sulphide is oxidized to lead sulphate by ozone – a very powerful oxidizing agent.

version of ordinary oxygen. Oxygen molecules have to be energized (usually electrically) before they come together to form ozone:

$$3O_2 + \text{energy} \rightarrow 2O_3.$$

When the ozone molecule is formed it is active and unstable – it easily reverts to ordinary oxygen. It is a very powerful oxidizing agent. For example, lead sulphide is oxidized to lead sulphate by ozone:

$$PbS + 4O_3 \rightarrow PbSO_4 + 4O_2$$

In this reaction, the ozone molecules lose a solitary oxygen atom, but in other reactions the whole molecule takes part. For example, sulphur dioxide is oxidized to sulphur trioxide, using all three oxygen atoms in the process:

$$3SO_2 + O_3 \rightarrow 3SO_3$$

Although ozone is present only in very small amounts in the air its powerful oxidizing action can, with time, cause cracking in rubber tyres. To overcome this, anti-oxidants are mixed with the rubber.

Preparation of Ozone

To form ozone, ordinary oxygen is passed through a tube where it is subjected to silent electrical discharges. The electrodes are covered with insulating materials (glass or mica) so that the discharge currents are kept low, and high voltage pulses are applied between the electrodes. This method has to be used so that the oxygen acquires the energy it needs to form the ozone, but at the same time the ozone does not become so hot that the molecules break up into ordinary oxygen.

Hydrogen

Like many other gases, hydrogen has no colour, no taste and no odour. What is so remarkable about it? Hydrogen is the lightest substance known: it weighs only one-fourteenth as much as an equal volume of air. It can be poured *upwards* from one jar to another. Because of its outstanding lightness it ought to be the best material for filling balloons. Unfortunately hydrogen has another remarkable feature – it is extremely inflammable. When hydrogen burns it combines with the oxygen in the air to form steam. At a very early stage in the Earth's history the hydrogen in the atmosphere must have burned to make steam which eventually cooled and condensed to water. That was how the oceans were formed.

Hardly any free hydrogen is left in the atmosphere today, for the tendency of hydrogen to combine with oxygen is very strong. The product of this combination is the oxide of hydrogen – we know it better as water. In fact the name hydrogen means 'water producer'. A mixture of hydrogen and air burns so rapidly that it explodes. It is *not* the same as the explosion of a hydrogen bomb, but it is very much like the explosion which occurs when a match is struck in a gas-filled room. As a matter of fact hydrogen forms a large percentage of ordinary household gas.

The risk of explosion and fire in hydrogen-filled airships is so great that these have become obsolete. But hydrogen is used for filling balloons which carry meteorological instruments up into the atmosphere.

A more important use of hydrogen is in the manufacture of synthetic ammonia. Ammonia is really a gas and the liquid sold as 'household ammonia' is the gas dissolved in water. Fertilizers and nitric acid are among the valuable substances obtained from ammonia which is itself obtained from hydrogen and nitrogen. In the Haber process for making ammonia, hydrogen is mixed with nitrogen. Then the mixture of gases is compressed to about $\frac{1}{200}$ of its original volume and passed over hot iron filings. The iron filings merely speed up the joining together of the hydrogen and the nitrogen.

Another important use of hydrogen is in the manufacture of margarine and cooking fats. Vegetable oils from olives and ground-nuts are converted into fats by treating them with hydrogen. Again the joining together of

The first air Channel crossing in 1875 was in a hydrogen-filled balloon.

From oil to margarine by hydrogen

Oil is heated in a closed vessel to about 200°C. A bubbling stream of hydrogen is fed through the oil which contains 1% of nickel filings. The hydrogen combines with the oil and turns it into fat. The nickel is a *catalyst* which speeds up the reaction. It is filtered out afterwards.

the hydrogen and the oils is speeded up by the presence of metal filings. In this case the metal used is nickel.

Hydrogen burns very readily in air. It burns even more readily in pure oxygen. By burning a mixture of hydrogen and oxygen in a special torch, temperatures around 2400°C can be obtained. At these fantastically high temperatures most metals melt. This fact is employed in the oxy-hydrogen welding and cutting of metals.

The uses of hydrogen just listed, with the addition of other less important applications throughout the world, require some 300,000 *tons* of hydrogen every year.

Water is a readily available source of hydrogen. By passing a current of electricity through water (with a little acid added to make it a better conductor) it can be split up into hydrogen and oxygen gases. This is, however, an expensive way of producing hydrogen and it is uneconomic to use it industrially.

Most of the hydrogen used in industry is manufactured from water by the Bosch process. The water is first turned to steam which is blown over red-hot iron filings. The iron combines with the oxygen part of the steam (steam is of course hydrogen oxide, H_2O) and the hydrogen gas is released. The steam is followed by a blast of 'water gas' (a mixture of hydrogen and carbon monoxide gases obtained by blowing steam through white-hot coke). This makes the iron hot again and removes the oxygen that has combined with it. The process then begins all over again.

Metals such as sodium and potassium, which are much more reactive than iron, will release hydrogen from water even when it is cold. A small piece of sodium metal dropped into water causes a violent reaction. The hydrogen produced catches fire and burns.

In the laboratory hydrogen is generally prepared by pouring dilute hydrochloric acid over a metal such as zinc. All acids contain hydrogen and in most cases this can be released

Water splitting by electrolysis into hydrogen and oxygen. The gas bubbles rise to the surface. Oxygen bubbles come from the wire connected to the positive terminal and hydrogen bubbles from the wire connected to the negative one. The experiment can be performed using salty water or water with a few drops of acid added.

as a gas by replacing it with a metal.

Hydrogen does not form many important compounds with metals. It is in many ways like a metal itself. Hydrogen passed over heated calcium metal reacts with it to form a colourless compound called calcium hydride or *hydrolith.* This is a very convenient source of hydrogen for use in emergencies, because water dropped onto hydrolith breaks it up into slaked lime and hydrogen gas.

It has already been mentioned that water, ammonia and all acids contain hydrogen. The number of hydrogen-containing substances is very large indeed because hydrogen will join with so many other elements. It has a strong tendency to join with carbon. The various products of this combination are called *hydrocarbons* and they are present in coal gas, gasoline, paraffin wax, etc. Substances containing hydrogen, carbon and oxygen combined together are almost countless – they have a special 'organic' branch of chemistry to themselves. Hydrogen occurs in a combined form in all living things. We do not breathe it, but we take it into our bodies as part of the food we eat.

The explosion in the 'top' container proves that the hydrogen has been poured upwards.

Hydrogen combines with many elements to form compounds called *hydrides*. The compounds of hydrogen with the more common non-metallic elements such as sulphur, chlorine, bromine and iodine yield acid solutions when they are dissolved in water. These acids give rise to series of metallic salts, such as the chlorides, bromides, sulphides and iodides. The term hydr*ide* should not be confused with the term hydr*ate*. This is the name given to compounds which bond chemically with molecules of water when it is available, without changing chemically themselves. The water is released if the compound is heated gently.

The hydrides can be divided into several groups according to their properties. These groups correspond quite closely to the position of the other element in the periodic table. The alkali and alkaline earth metals and the halogens (non-metals) are at opposite ends of the horizontal rows or *periods* in the table, and the hydrides which they form behave in different ways. This is because the hydrides of the alkali and alkaline earth metals are ionic, with positively-charged metal ions and negatively-charged hydride ions, whereas the hydrides of the halogens are covalent. In these, the atoms are held together in molecules and no ions are present. Between these extremes are many more hydrides of metals and non-metals with intermediate properties.

Ionic Metal Hydrides

All the hydrides of the alkali and alkaline earth metals are strong reducing agents. They react with water, some of them violently. Hydrogen gas is liberated and the hydroxide of the metal is formed. The reaction between water and calcium hydride is one of the least violent. For this reason calcium hydride is used as a convenient source of portable hydrogen.

The hydrides of this group are fairly stable, colourless, crystalline com-

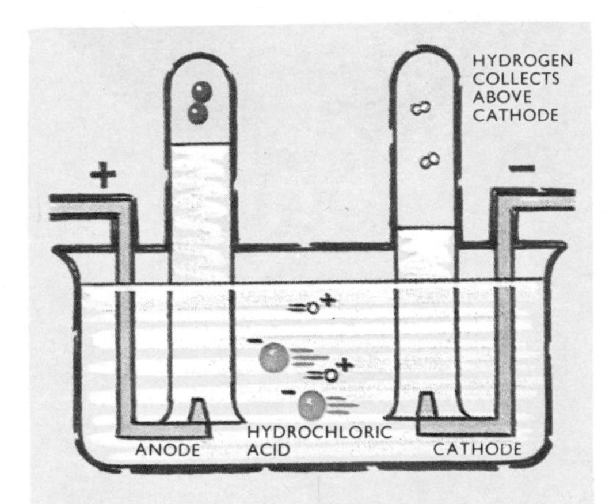

The hydrogen in lithium hydride behaves rather like the halogens – lithium hydride (*below*) ionizes to give *negatively* charged *hydride* ions. Hydrogen gas can be collected above the anode of the cell. In contrast, dilute hydrochloric acid (*above*) contains *positively* charged *hydrogen* ions. When it is electrolysed, hydrogen gas is liberated at the cathode.

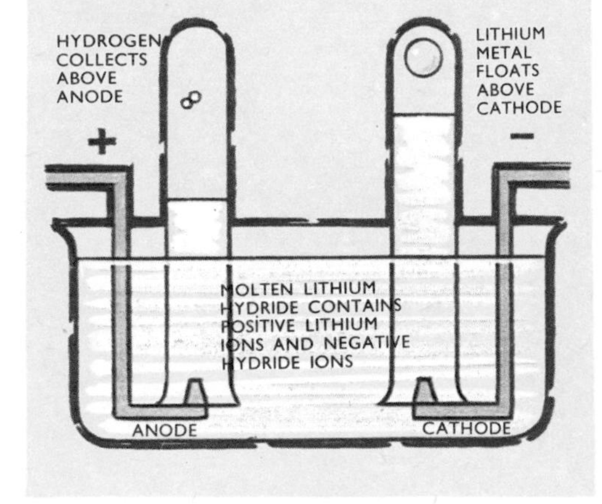

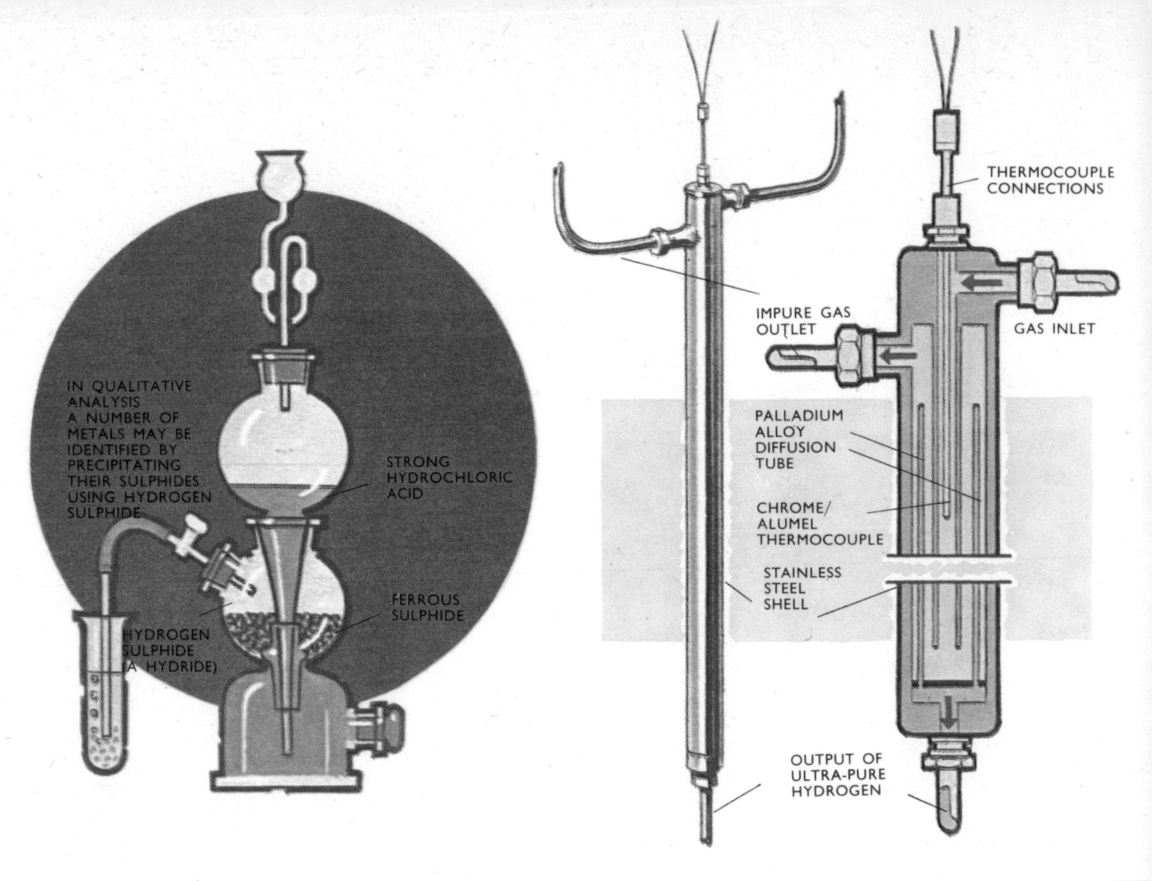

The principal hydride of sulphur (hydrogen sulphide) is an important reagent which is used in qualitative analysis.

External view and cutaway of a platinum alloy diffusion cell used for purifying hydrogen. The cell operates at about 400°C and 30 atmospheres pressure.

pounds which resemble, in some ways, the chlorides and iodides of the same metals. They are usually prepared by passing hydrogen under pressure over the heated metal.

Other Metal Hydrides

Although it is doubtful whether true chemical compounds are formed between hydrogen and some metals, it is certainly true that hydrogen gas is absorbed by many metals when they are heated in the gas. The actual mechanism for taking up hydrogen is in doubt and may very well vary between the different metals.

The power of the metal palladium to absorb hydrogen is outstanding. Powdered palladium which has been kept in an atmosphere of hydrogen at 100°C for three hours, and then left to cool in the gas for ninety minutes absorbs as much as 650 times its own volume of the gas. Advantage is taken of this in the production of very pure hydrogen.

Hydrides of Non-Metals

This group includes compounds such as hydrogen chloride, hydrogen iodide, hydrogen sulphide and water. Some of these compounds (e.g. hydrogen iodide and water) can be prepared by direct combination between the elements concerned. However, hydrogen chloride and hydrogen sulphide can be obtained much more easily by the action of a strong acid (not nitric acid) on an appropriate metallic salt. For instance, hydrogen

PERIODIC TABLE OF THE ELEMENTS

I	II	III	IV	V	VI	VII	0
						H	He
Li	Be	B	C	N	O	F	Ne
Na	Mg	Al	Si	P	S	Cl	Ar

IA	IIA	IIIA	IVA	VA	VIA	VIIA	–	VIII	–	IB	IIB	IIIB	IVB	VB	VIB	VIIB	0
K	Ca	Sc	Ti	V	Cr	Mn	Fe	Co	Ni	Cu	Zn	Ga	Ge	As	Se	Br	Kr
Rb	Sr	Y	Zr	Nb	Mo	Tc	Ru	Rh	Pd	Ag	Cd	In	Sn	Sb	Te	I	Xe
Cs	Ba	La	Hf	Ta	W	Re	Os	Ir	Pt	Au	Hg	Tl	Pb	Bi	Po	At	Rn
Fr	Ra	Ac															

IONIC METAL HYDRIDES — TRANSITION METAL HYDRIDES — INTERMEDIATE METAL HYDRIDES — COVALENT HYDRIDES — INERT GASES

The position of an element in the periodic table (*above*) is a good guide to the type of hydride it will form. The alkali and alkaline earth metals (on the left of the table) form ionic hydrides in which hydrogen is the acid radical. The non-metals give rise to covalent hydrides.

chloride is generally prepared by heating sodium chloride and concentrated sulphuric acid.

When certain of these hydrides are dissolved in water they form acid solutions and positively charged hydrogen ions are produced. These hydrides give rise to well defined series of salts – chlorides, bromides, iodides and sulphides.

The hydrides of oxygen (water and hydrogen peroxide) do not appear to resemble any of the other hydrides very closely. Water occupies an almost unique position – many of its unusual properties are due to hydrogen bonding between molecules.

The hydrides of carbon (the *hydrocarbons*) are probably the most important hydrides in this group. This almost limitless range of compounds is present in crude oil, or is produced at various stages in refining. The hydrocarbons are valuable as fuels and, even more important, as the raw materials used in the manufacture of a vast range of substances including plastics and artificial fibres.

There are *aliphatic* (or chain) hydrocarbons in which hydrogen atoms are attached to a chain of carbon atoms, while the basic unit of the *aromatic* hydrocarbons is a ring of six carbon atoms with one hydrogen atom attached to each.

The hydrides of two other non-metals – nitrogen and phosphorus – are also quite important and have certain properties in common. Both ammonia (NH_3) and phosphine (PH_3) are alkaline and form halides, though in these respects phosphine is much weaker. Ammonia actually gives rise to an ion – the ammonium ion – which behaves in a similar manner to the ions of the alkali metals.

Water is a very abundant and very widely distributed chemical *compound.* It consists of the *elements* hydrogen and oxygen combined together in the proportions of two atoms to one atom respectively.

When hydrogen burns in oxygen, water is formed, a greatly different sort of substance from either hydrogen or oxygen, so obviously the properties of both hydrogen and oxygen have been changed by their combination.

It is quite easy to show that water consists of hydrogen and oxygen by means of *electrolysis* (splitting of a substance by an electric current). Water (containing a little sulphuric acid) is put in the apparatus shown, so as to completely fill the side tubes. Pure water does not conduct a current well and a little acid is added to enable it to do so. The acid does not change or get used up during the experiment. With the taps closed, the platinum plates (*electrodes*) are connected to a battery (platinum is an expensive metal, used because it does not react during electrolytic processes). When the current passes through the water it splits the water

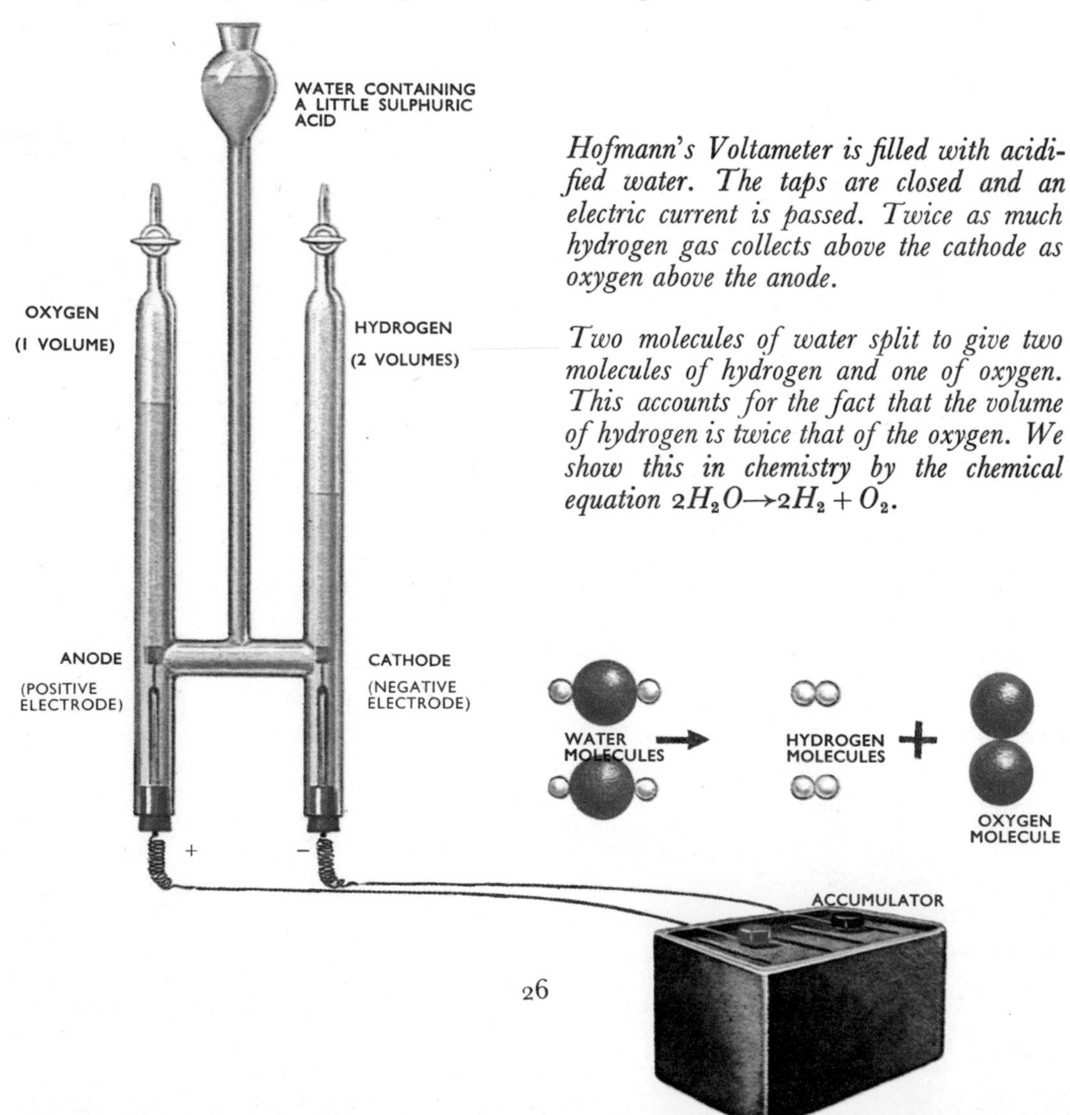

Hofmann's Voltameter is filled with acidified water. The taps are closed and an electric current is passed. Twice as much hydrogen gas collects above the cathode as oxygen above the anode.

Two molecules of water split to give two molecules of hydrogen and one of oxygen. This accounts for the fact that the volume of hydrogen is twice that of the oxygen. We show this in chemistry by the chemical equation $2H_2O \rightarrow 2H_2 + O_2$.

into two gases, bubbles of which rise from the electrodes. From the cathode (the negative electrode) bubbles rise and the gas can be shown to be hydrogen. These bubbles form a volume which is twice the volume of the gas rising from the other electrode called the anode (positive). The smaller volume of gas can be shown to be oxygen. Oxygen is tested by means of a glowing wooden splint which bursts into flame. Hydrogen when mixed with air explodes when a lighted taper is brought into contact with it.

Two *molecules* of water split to give two molecules of hydrogen gas and one molecule of oxygen gas. This is because *two* oxygen atoms are needed to make an oxygen molecule. By pairing up and sharing two of each other's electrons *both* oxygen atoms gain complete outer electron-shells.

Note. A *molecule* is two or more atoms joined together and is the smallest particle of a substance which normally exists.

H_2O represents one molecule of water which consists of two atoms of hydrogen and one atom of oxygen all joined together into a single unit by electrical forces.

Water is very abundant but it can be made by mixing hydrogen gas with half its volume of oxygen gas and igniting the two. This is the reverse process to the electrolysis of water and the reaction can be represented by the following equation:

$$2H_2+O_2 \rightarrow 2H_2O$$

Actually steam is first formed which on cooling condenses to water droplets. By allowing the flame of burning hydrogen to be close to a cold surface, steam formed will be condensed to drops which can be collected and

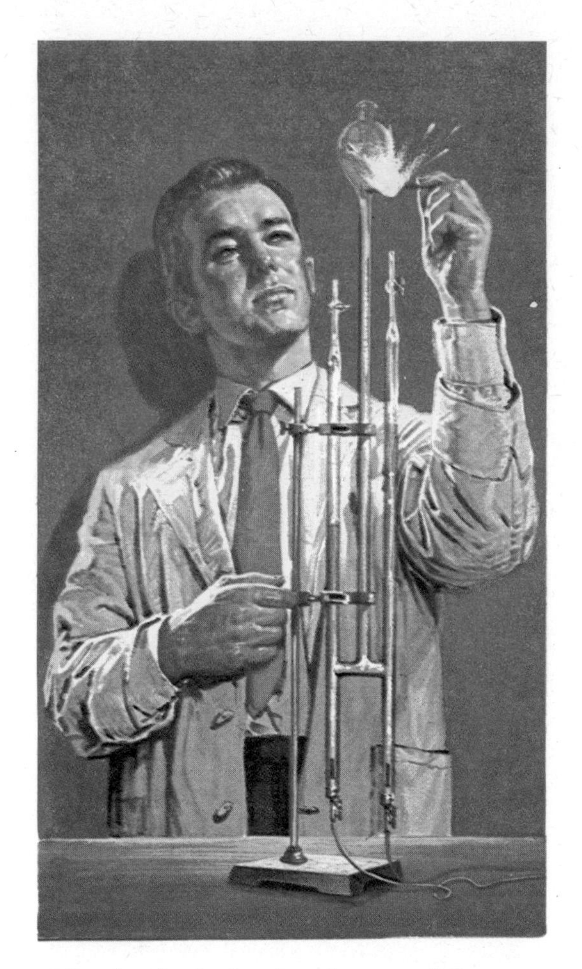

The chemist is showing that one of the gases collected is oxygen. This gas makes a glowing splint of wood burst into flame.

tested. All physical and chemical tests on the liquid show it to be water. To make sure that water collected is due to the burning (*combustion*) of hydrogen and *not* due to the gas being moist, the gas is dried by passing through a substance which dries it (calcium chloride).

One important fact about water is that it is *stable*. (A substance is said to be stable if it is difficult to break up or change in any other way.) However, an electric current *decomposes* it, and two very reactive metals like potassium and sodium react vigorously with cold water, re-

Both pictures illustrate copper sulphate. The crystal, although it is perfectly dry to the touch, owes its colour and shape to the fact that its molecules are bonded with water molecules.

leasing hydrogen gas from it. Some other metals will react with water, but less rapidly; calcium is one of these metals. Magnesium, zinc and iron react with steam but are not affected by pure cold water.

Many minerals and crystals which are perfectly dry to the touch nevertheless contain water which is combined chemically, and *not* simply mixed. Substances containing water so combined are said to be *hydrated*, e.g. blue copper sulphate crystals. If blue crystals of copper sulphate are heated in a test-tube, the water is driven off and will condense at the cold mouth of a test-tube; the loss of water causes the crystals to lose both their shape and blue colour and to change to a greyish-white powder called *anhydrous* copper sulphate. (Anhydrous means without water.)

The three *physical states* of water are steam (gas), water (liquid) and ice (solid). Each behaves the same way *chemically* but they are *physically* different.

Steam is composed of separate H_2O molecules, whereas ice has an ordered structure and can be considered to be one large molecule made up of many water molecules specially *bonded* together by *hydrogen bonds*. Water is *polar* because the negatively-charged electrons seem to be attracted more towards the oxygen atoms, making them negatively charged with respect to the hydrogen atoms which become positively charged. The positive hydrogen of one water molecule thus attracts the negative oxygen of a neighbouring molecule, forming a hydrogen bond. This bond is a weak one, but ice can be considered to be a large single molecule rather than a 'package' of separate H_2O molecules. Crystal chemistry shows that H_2O molecules in ice are arranged so that each oxygen atom has four hydrogen atoms as fairly close neighbours, two attached by strong *covalent* bonds (i.e. by shared electrons) and two more by the weaker hydrogen bonding at a greater distance. This leads to an open structure, i.e. one with relatively large holes in it. When ice melts, some of the hydrogen bonds are broken and more close packing results. Thus water has a greater density than ice and this is why ice floats in water.

The First Three Families and the Transition Elements

CHAPTER THREE

Group 1. The Alkali Metals

THE term alkali metals is the name given to the family of low density metals lithium, sodium, potassium, rubidium and caesium. The ammonium *radical* is sometimes included in the same group as well since there are a number of features which ammonium salts have in common with the corresponding salts of the alkali metals.

These metals are so reactive that none of them occurs free in nature. Potassium, for instance, reacts so violently with water that the hydrogen gas which it liberates is set alight by the heat given out in the reaction.

Of the alkali metals, the salts of sodium are by far the most abundant. Sea water contains about 27 parts per thousand by weight of sodium chloride. There are also a number of deposits of sodium compounds in the solid state—rock salt (sodium chloride) is found in Cheshire, Chile saltpetre (sodium nitrate) in South America and borax (sodium borate) in California. Potassium chloride along with sodium chloride and magnesium chloride occurs in the Stassfurt deposit in East Germany, and this is the principal source of potassium, although potassium carbonate can be recovered from the ash left behind after plants have been burnt. In comparison, the salts of lithium, rubidium and caesium are rare.

Sodium and potassium were first isolated in 1807 by Sir Humphry Davy. His original method was to pass an electric current through the molten hydroxide and as a result of electrolysis the metal was collected above the cathode (the negative electrode). This method is not now favoured on a commercial scale and it has been replaced by another electrolytic process in which molten sodium chloride decomposes as a result of the passage of a *direct* current of electricity.

As the melting point of sodium chloride (801°C.) is quite close to the boiling point of sodium metal, calcium chloride is often added to the sodium chloride to give a mixture which melts at about 600°C. In the *Downs process* a circular carbon anode is surrounded by a cylindrical iron cathode. The whole 'cell' is enclosed in a fire-brick box to conserve as much of the heat as possible.

When an electric current is passed through molten sodium chloride, the negatively charged chloride ions migrate towards the positively charged anode (unlike charges attract one another). On arrival at the anode each chloride ion gives up its spare electron which helps to make up the electron deficiency on the anode. It is by this movement of charged ions that the flow of electrons which constitutes an electric current can pass through certain liquids. As soon as the chloride *ions* have lost their charges, they become uncharged chlorine *atoms* which join up in pairs to become *molecules* of chlorine gas. These rise through the molten sodium chloride and are collected under the hood and led away as a valuable by-product.

While this is going on the positively charged sodium ions travel to the negatively charged cathode, where each one gains an electron to become a neutral sodium atom. Since sodium metal is less dense than fused sodium chloride, it rises into the ring-shaped space above the cylindrical iron cathode, whence it is drawn off into a storage container.

There are few technical advantages of potassium over sodium, so the latter element is used wherever possible. Only small quantities of potassium are produced commercially, since sodium can be produced much more cheaply from its more abundant raw materials. When required, potassium can be obtained by the electrolysis of molten potassium chloride.

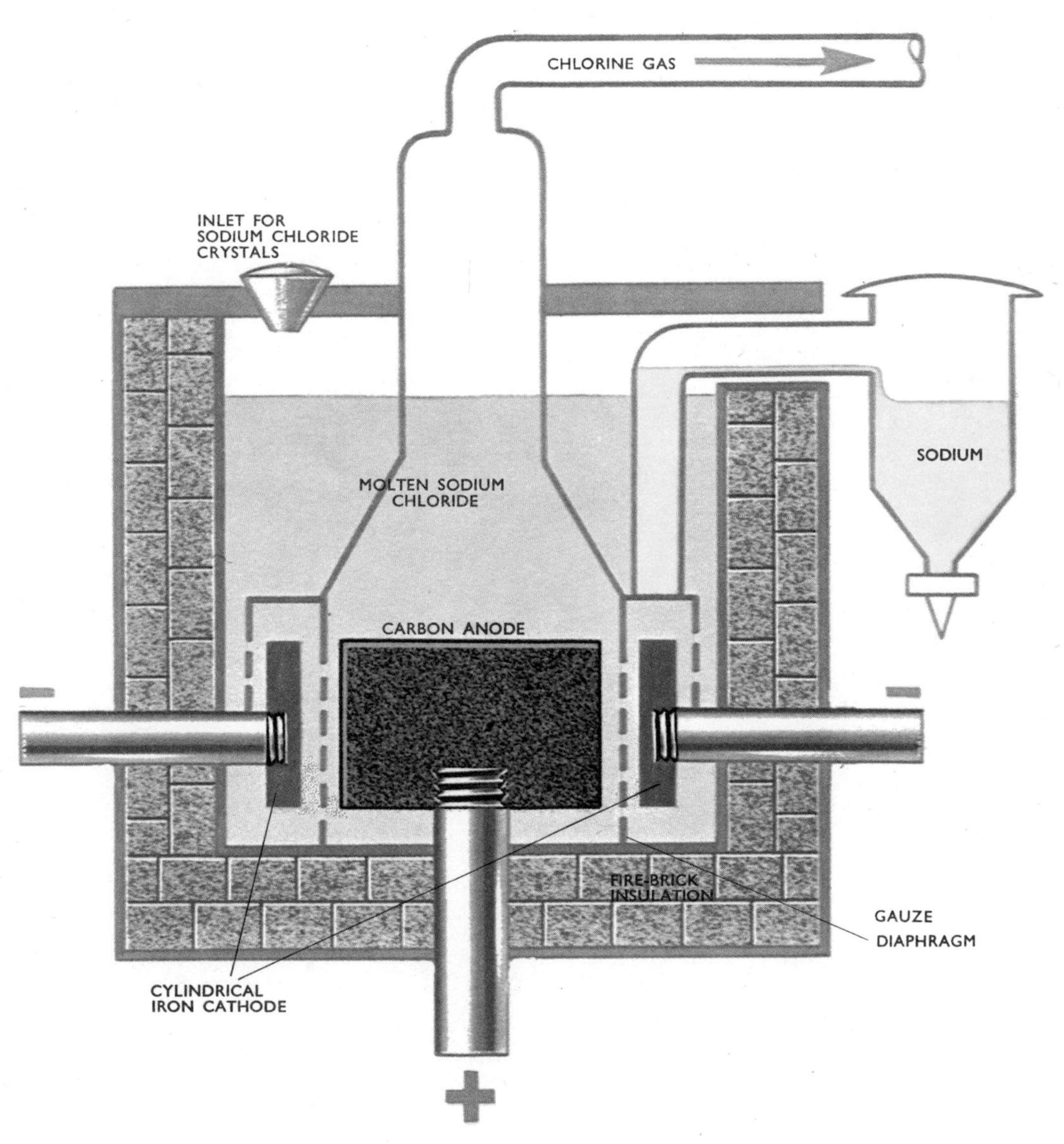

The Downs Cell in which sodium and chlorine are produced on a commercial scale by electrolysing molten sodium chloride.

An alternative method is to use the replacement reaction between sodium and fused potassium chloride:

Na	+	KCl	→	K	+	NaCl
SODIUM		POTASSIUM CHLORIDE		POTASSIUM		SODIUM CHLORIDE

Both sodium and potassium are very reactive and have similar properties. The main difference between them is that potassium is more reactive than sodium. They are both silvery white metals when freshly cut but a film soon forms over the metallic surfaces. They are so soft that they can be cut with a knife.

Both metals readily combine with the halogens (fluorine, chlorine, bromine and iodine), phosphorus, sulphur, oxygen and hydrogen. The hydrides of sodium and potassium (NaH and KH) which are used as reducing agents in organic chemistry, are interesting in that the hydrogen in the molecule exists as a *negatively* charged hydride *ion* (H^-).

When put into water sodium and potassium react violently to form the hydroxide of the metal (caustic soda or caustic potash) while hydrogen is set free. So much heat is given out by the reaction with potassium that the hydrogen ignites and burns with a lilac flame. On account of this property these metals must be stored under kerosene or in air-tight containers. On no account should they be touched with bare hands.

Sodium and potassium are essential elements for the healthy growth of animals, while potassium is essential for plants. Sodium is finding increasing use in sodium-vapour lamps for street lighting because the vapour gives out a characteristic intense yellow light. Various alloys of lithium have special applications ranging from bearing metal (lithium-lead) to aluminium alloys with great strength and resistance to corrosion. Caesium is used in photoelectric cells.

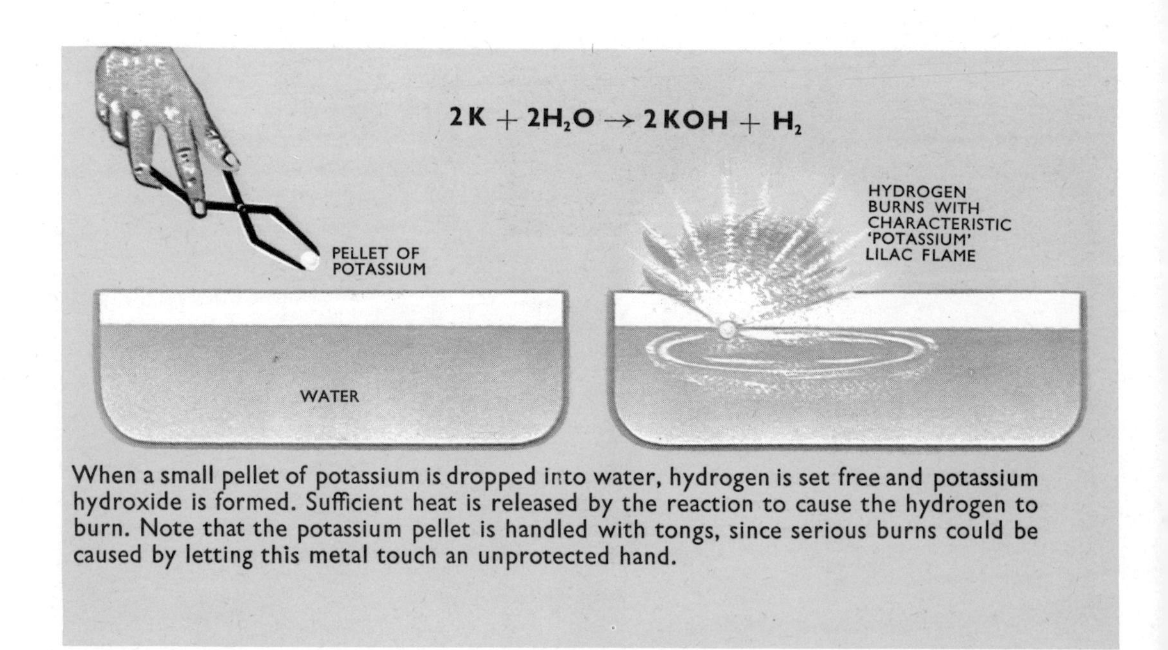

When a small pellet of potassium is dropped into water, hydrogen is set free and potassium hydroxide is formed. Sufficient heat is released by the reaction to cause the hydrogen to burn. Note that the potassium pellet is handled with tongs, since serious burns could be caused by letting this metal touch an unprotected hand.

The principal sodium compounds found in Nature are sodium chloride (in sea water and as rock salt), sodium nitrate (as Chile saltpetre) and complex alumino-silicates such as sodium felspar. As a result of weathering, the latter class of compound breaks down to yield clay and sodium carbonate. Sodium carbonate is also obtained from the ash left after burning marine plants.

Almost without exception sodium and all sodium compounds are ionic. Considerable use is made of the solubility of sodium salts, particularly in softening water. The ion exchange compounds such as zeolites are complex sodium aluminium silicates. When water, which is hard because it contains calcium ions, flows through the resin column the sodium and calcium ions exchange places and the water is thereby softened. Thus the calcium salts which form scums have been removed. The action of soap as a means of softening water is similar. Soap, the sodium salts of various organic acids, reacts with the calcium ions in the solution to give insoluble calcium compounds which settle out as scum.

Sodium peroxide, a yellow solid which is prepared by passing air, free from water and carbon dioxide, over hot sodium (300°C), has several valuable uses. In particular it can be used to remove carbon dioxide from air in confined spaces as in submerged submarines.

$$2Na_2O_2 + 2CO_2 \rightarrow 2Na_2CO_3 + O_2$$

sodium peroxide + carbon dioxide → sodium carbonate + oxygen

Sodium peroxide also gives oxygen by a reaction with water, which method provides a useful source of small quantities of oxygen in the laboratory.

Sodium sulphate (Na_2SO_4) which is made commercially by the action

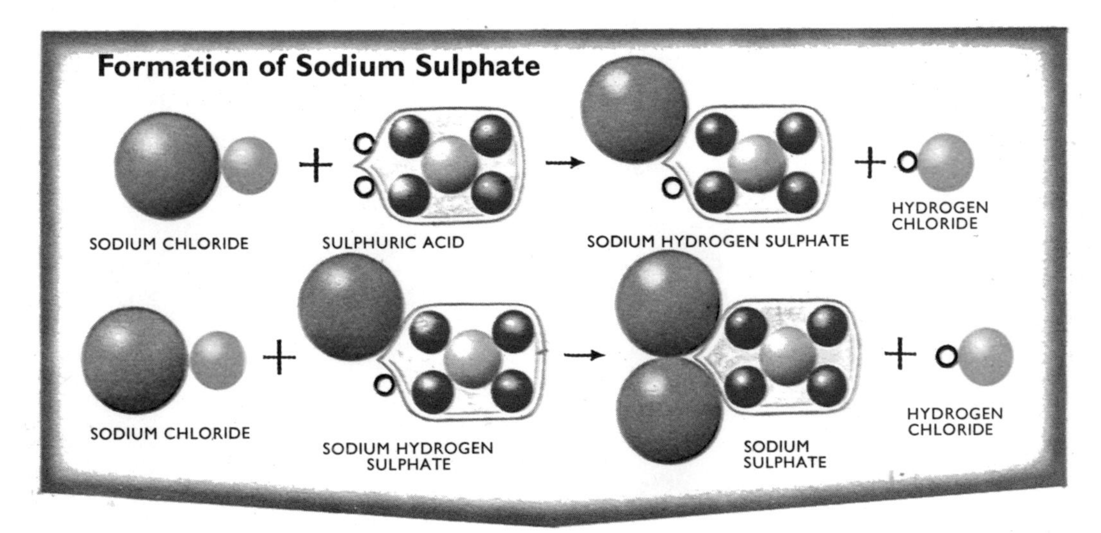

—C

Sodium sulphate is manufactured in two stages. First, sodium hydrogen sulphate is obtained by the action of concentrated sulphuric acid on sodium chloride in the cast-iron pot. The resultant pasty mass is then transferred into the muffle furnace, where the second reaction takes place.

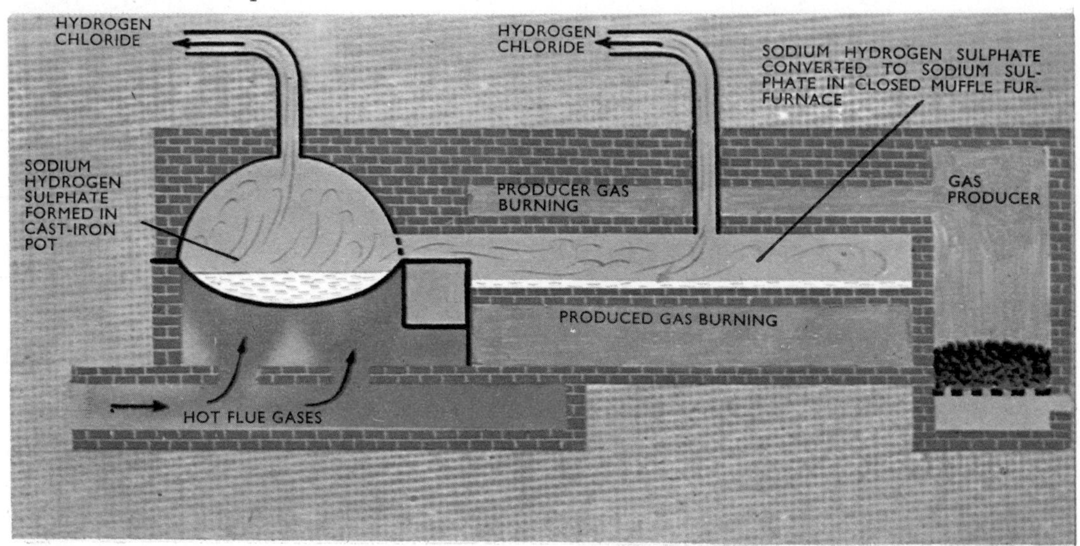

of hot concentrated sulphuric acid on sodium chloride, crystallizes with ten molecules of water for each molecule of the salt. It is known as Glauber's salt and large quantities are now required in the manufacture of synthetic detergents. Sodium sulphate is also used in dyeing and in the textile industry.

Sodium carbonate (Na_2CO_3) is made in very large quantities by the Solvay process. In this, sodium chloride and calcium carbonate are the raw materials, and sodium carbonate and calcium chloride the products. The process by which this apparently simple change takes place is, however, quite complicated. Sodium chloride solution is saturated with ammonia, and carbon dioxide (made by heating calcium carbonate) is then blown through it. Sodium bicarbonate is formed as a solid and can be filtered out, leaving ammonium chloride solution. The bicarbonate is heated to give sodium carbonate. Calcium hydroxide is added to the ammonium chloride solution to regenerate the ammonia and give calcium chloride. Most sodium carbonate is used for making glass.

Sodium thiosulphate ($Na_2S_2O_3$) is much used by photographers under the name of 'hypo'. It reacts with silver bromide to form a complex compound which is soluble in water. In this way any silver bromide remaining on an exposed film (in those areas which have received light, silver bromide will have been reduced to silver) can be washed away. Sodium thiosulphate is used in analysis for finding the quantity of iodine in a sample. The iodine is converted to sodium iodide:

$$\underset{\text{sodium thiosulphate}}{2Na_2S_2O_3} + \underset{\text{iodine}}{I_2} \longrightarrow \underset{\text{sodium iodide}}{2NaI} + \underset{\text{sodium tetrathionate}}{Na_2S_4O_6}$$

The point at which all the iodine has reacted can be easily found by adding a small quantity of starch. This gives an intense blue coloration in the presence of traces of iodine.

CHAPTER FOUR

Group 2

Calcium

Although the metal calcium is not itself particularly important commercially, a number of its compounds have been used extensively in various industries over a period of many years. Limestone (calcium carbonate) is an essential ingredient for the manufacture of both Portland cement and glass. The mortar which is used in bonding bricks together is made by mixing slaked lime (calcium hydroxide) and sand with water until a thick paste is obtained.

Anhydrite (one of the naturally occurring forms of calcium sulphate) is now being used as a source of sulphur for the manufacture of sulphuric acid. Calcium phosphate is an essential constituent of bone, containing as it does some 58% of the compound.

Calcium does not occur free in Nature, but calcium-containing compounds are widespread and available in large quantities. Amongst the naturally occurring calcium compounds is calcium carbonate which is the principal constituent of limestone, marble, coral, and chalk. Calcium sulphate occurs as anhydrite and gypsum. Fluorspar, calcium fluoride, is a valuable source of fluorine gas as well as of the element calcium.

In common with the other reactive metals which are related to it, metallic calcium may be obtained by the electrolysis of fused calcium chloride. To lower the melting point a small quantity of calcium fluoride may be added. The calcium chloride comes as a by-product from the Solvay Process for the manufacture of sodium carbonate, but since the demand for calcium is very small compared with the amount of calcium chloride produced, this is not a very profitable outlet for the calcium chloride.

Metallic calcium is usually obtained from molten calcium chloride by electrolysis. The calcium is deposited on the water-cooled cathode.

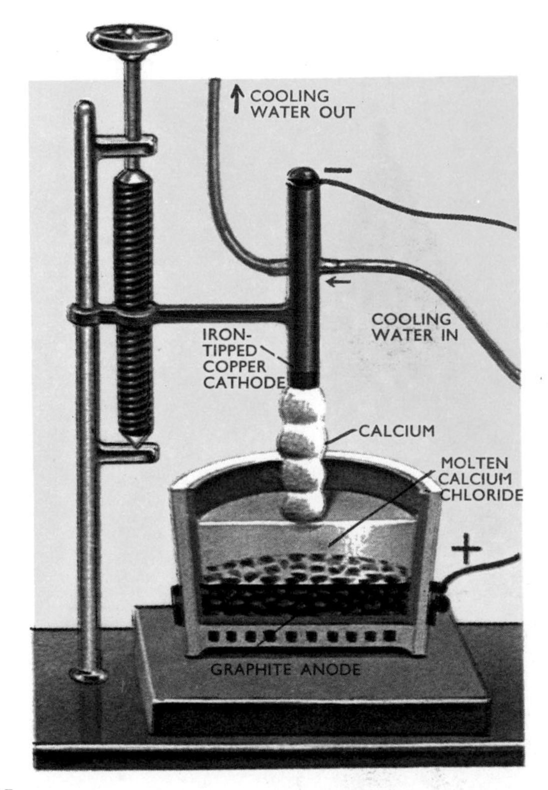

The electrolysis is carried out in a graphite-lined vessel which also serves as the anode of the cell. A water-cooled copper tube with an iron tip is used as the cathode. As calcium is deposited on the iron tip of the cathode, the cathode is raised slowly so that only the lower surface of the calcium is in the melt.

Calcium is a silvery white metal. It is harder than lead but not much more dense than water. If exposed to the air it rapidly becomes covered with a layer of white calcium oxide. The metal may be burned in air and does so with a characteristic brick-red flame. This same colour is observed when any calcium compounds are heated on the tip of a platinum wire in a Bunsen burner flame.

Hydrogen gas and calcium hydroxide are formed when calcium is put into cold water. Since the calcium hydroxide is not very soluble in water it tends to settle out of the solution as a fine white precipitate.

$$\underset{\text{calcium}}{Ca} + \underset{\text{water}}{2H_2O} \rightarrow \underset{\text{calcium hydroxide}}{Ca(OH)_2} + \underset{\text{hydrogen}}{H_2}$$

Calcium is very reactive and will combine directly with dry chlorine, hydrogen, nitrogen and sulphur to form calcium chloride ($CaCl_2$), calcium hydride (CaH_2), calcium nitride (Ca_3N_2) and calcium sulphide (CaS) respectively.

Calcium is used as a reducing agent both in organic chemistry and in the extraction of metals from their compounds. It is also used as a drying agent for removing the last traces of water from organic substances such as alcohol. The usual method of keeping *absolute* alcohol free of water is to have calcium shavings in the bottom of the bottle, though these must first be removed if the bottle should subsequently be rinsed with water.

Calcium oxide (quicklime) is manufactured on a large scale by lime burning: limestone (calcium carbonate) is heated in tall furnaces known

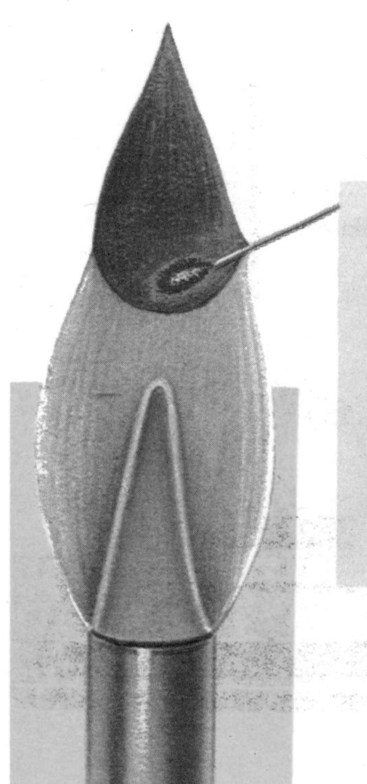

Compounds of calcium may be detected by the brick red colour which they give to a bunsen burner flame.

CALCIUM COMPOUNDS

Common Name	*Chemical Name*	*Uses*
Quicklime	calcium oxide	drying agent.
Slaked lime	calcium hydroxide	making mortar; neutralizing acid soil.
Chalk Limestone Marble	calcium carbonate	manufacture of cement, glass, lime.
—	calcium chloride	manufacture of metallic calcium; drying agent.
—	calcium carbide	manufacture of acetylene.
Anhydrite Gypsum Plaster of Paris	calcium sulphate	source of sulphur; 'setting' broken bones.

as *lime kilns*. The heat needed to bring about this reversible reaction is obtained by burning producer gas in air. Quicklime is removed from the foot of the kiln and the carbon dioxide escapes from the top.

$$\underset{\text{calcium carbonate}}{CaCO_3} \rightleftarrows \underset{\text{calcium oxide}}{CaO} + \underset{\text{carbon dioxide}}{CO_2}$$

Since much heat is given out when calcium oxide is added to water, it is frequently converted into slaked lime (calcium hydroxide) before being

$$\underset{\text{calcium oxide}}{CaO} + \underset{\text{water}}{H_2O} \rightarrow \underset{\text{calcium hydroxide}}{Ca(OH)_2}$$

used. In addition to its uses in the building trade, slaked lime is used extensively in agriculture for 'sweetening' acid soils. The calcium hydroxide is mildly alkaline and neutralizes the acid. Slaked lime is also an important raw material in the manufacture of a large number of other industrial chemical compounds.

As already stated large quantities of calcium chloride are obtained as a by-product from the Solvay Process. This salt may also be obtained by the action of hydrochloric acid on calcium oxide, calcium hydroxide or calcium carbonate. Some commercial calcium chloride is used in the preparation of metallic calcium, but a rather larger portion is converted to the anhydrous (water free) state by heating. (Crystalline calcium chloride contains six molecules of water with every molecule of calcium chloride.) As anhydrous calcium chloride readily absorbs water it is frequently used as a drying agent.

Calcium carbide is an interesting compound in that it is itself inorganic, but can be used as a source of organic compounds. It is manufactured by heating a mixture of coke and quick-

Anhydrous calcium chloride is used as a drying agent. In this desiccator hot crucibles and evaporating dishes are able to cool down without absorbing water vapour since the air has been dried.

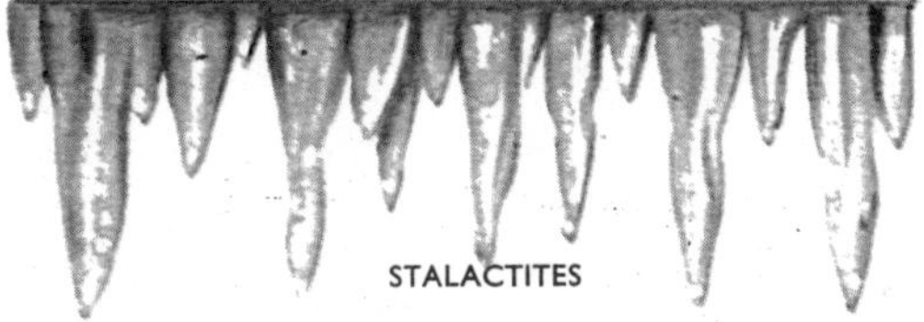

When water which contains dissolved carbon dioxide flows over limestone soluble calcium bicarbonate is formed. Stalactites and stalagmites build up in limestone caves as a result of such a solution dripping down and evaporating.

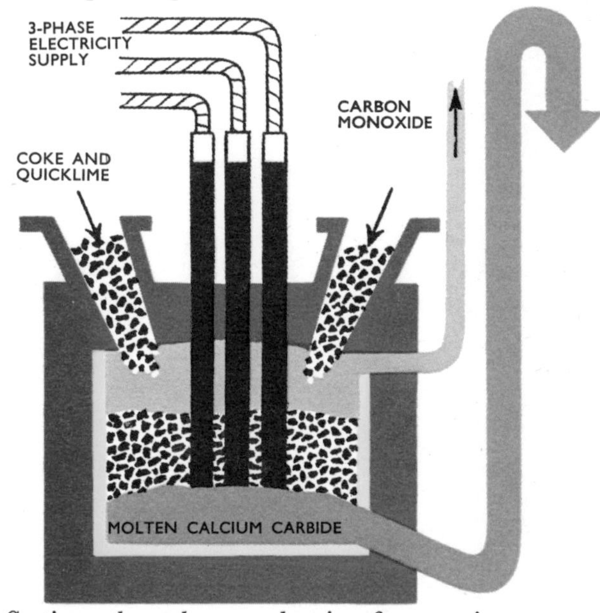

Section through an electric furnace in which calcium carbide is made from coke (carbon) and quicklime (calcium oxide).

The principal raw materials used in the manufacture of the general-purpose glass for bottles and jars are sand (silicon oxide), limestone (calcium carbonate) and soda ash (sodium carbonate). Here the raw materials are being fed from hoppers to the furnaces at the beginning of the process.

lime at 2500°C. in an electric furnace.

CaO	+	$3C$	→	CaC_2	+	CO
calcium oxide		carbon		calcium carbide		carbon monoxide

By adding water to calcium carbide (a greyish solid) the inflammable gas acetylene is set free:

CaC_2	+	$2H_2O$	→	C_2H_2	+	$Ca(OH)_2$
calcium carbide		water		acetylene		calcium hydroxide

Calcium carbide was formerly used as a convenient source of acetylene for bicycle lamps and car lamps. Acetylene is now manufactured using the same method on a large scale and then converted into acetaldehyde, ethyl alcohol and acetic acid.

Calcium sulphate is found in Nature as an anhydrous salt (anhydrite) and a dihydrate (gypsum). When gypsum is heated to 120°C. it loses some of the combined water:

$2CaSO_4.2H_2O$	→	$(CaSO_4)_2.H_2O$	+	$3H_2O$
gypsum		Plaster of Paris		water

This 'hemihydrate' is known as *plaster of Paris* which sets to a hard mass after water has been mixed with it. During the setting process the plaster expands slightly, so ensuring a sharp copy of any mould into which it is poured. It is widely used as an ingredient of the plaster for use inside buildings both on walls and for ornaments. Gypsum is also used in the manufacture of the crayons ('chalk') used on blackboards, and in the plaster used in orthopaedics (for 'setting' broken bones) and dentistry. Calcium sulphate is slightly soluble in water and is one cause of permanent hardness of water.

It will be seen in the following text that calcium is in many ways similar to strontium and barium. This is to be expected as they are in the same family in the periodic table.

Strontium and Barium

No firework display is complete without compounds of the elements strontium and barium. They are not responsible for the explosions themselves but are used in small quantities to add colour to the flames produced by the burning of other chemical substances. Vivid deep crimson flames receive their colour from strontium compounds. Crimson strontium flames are also used in flares and tracer bullets. The tracer bullets clearly show the path that would be taken by a real bullet. Barium compounds give a rather beautiful greenish-yellow (apple-green) coloured flame.

The distinctive flame colours of the compounds of strontium and barium make it easy for the chemist to detect their presence during analysis. If a clean platinum wire is held in a roaring Bunsen flame it does not change the flame colour at all. If the wire is first dipped into concentrated hydrochloric acid, then into a little of the sample being analysed and finally held in the Bunsen flame sometimes the flame will be coloured. Barium compounds give apple-green flames and strontium compounds give crimson flames.

Although their flames are so different, strontium and barium are two very similar members of a family of elements. The metal calcium is the head of this small family. It is not surprising that they are chemically similar, for reference to the periodic table of elements shows that calcium, strontium and barium all have completely full inner shells of electrons and two electrons in the outermost shell. The difference between them is that barium has one more full electron shell than strontium which in turn has one full shell more than calcium.

The similarity between these ele-

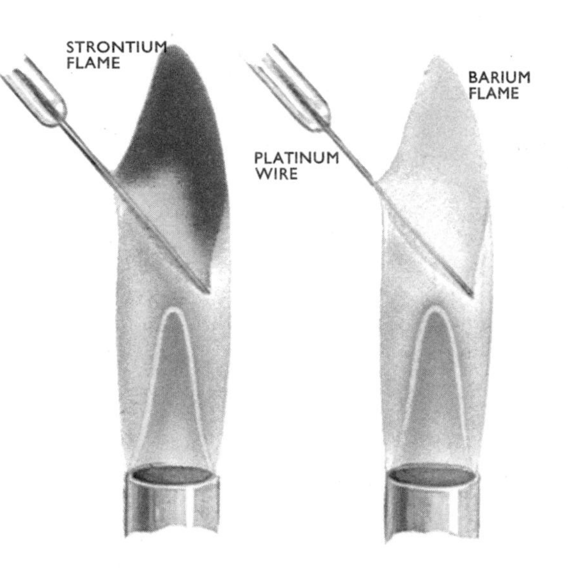

Flame test. Strontium flames are crimson and barium flames are apple green.

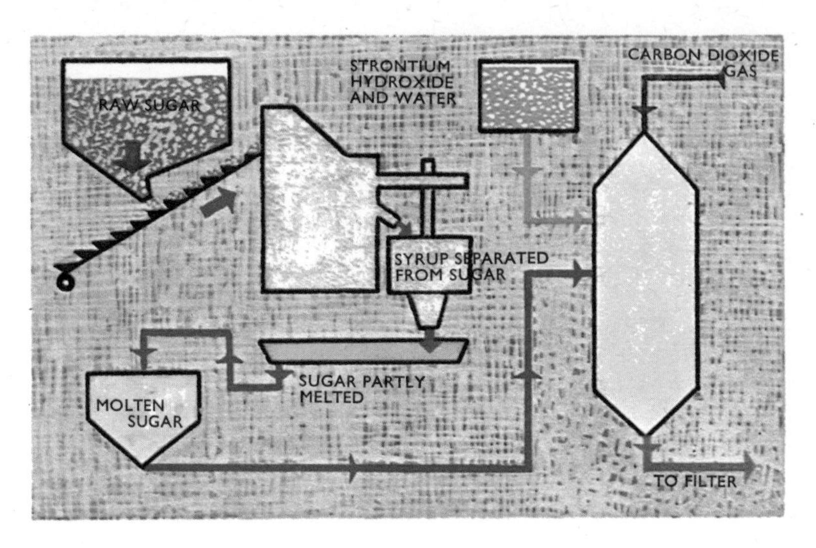

Beet sugar being purified with strontium hydroxide. Solid particles of strontium saccharate form from which carbon dioxide regenerates the sugar.

ments has been the cause of trouble. A radioactive isotope of strontium, known as strontium 90 is one of the products of nuclear explosions. Because of its similarity to calcium, this radioactive strontium can take the place of the much-needed calcium in milk. There have been several occasions when large quantities of contaminated milk have had to be poured away to avoid the risk of harmful effects which might result if it were drunk.

Both strontium and barium are highly reactive metals and because of this are never found free in nature but always in the form of compounds. Among other methods the metals can be obtained by the electrolysis of certain of their compounds. But as the metals themselves have little use they are extracted only on a small scale. Strontium has no commercial uses but some barium is used in removing the last traces of air from radio valves. Barium is also made into an alloy with nickel. This alloy is used in sparking plugs and the cathodes of radio valves because when it is heated it releases large quantities of electrons.

Both metals are silvery white in colour and are quite soft. Strontium is about as soft as lead and barium is softer still. In air strontium oxidizes fairly rapidly whereas barium is much more reactive and bursts into flame.

Although the metals themselves have few uses this is certainly not true of their compounds.

Strontium compounds.

Two strontium compounds occur naturally. These are the sulphate and the carbonate. Strontium sulphate or celestite crystals are very beautiful. They are usually colourless but sometimes have a soft tinge of blue. They can be confused with barite, the sulphate of barium. Crystals of strontianite, strontium carbonate, are yellowish white in colour. They, too, are sometimes confused with the carbonate of barium, witherite. Flame testing with a small piece of crystal soon settles the confusion. Other strontium compounds are manufactured from the carbonate and sulphate.

Strontium hydroxide is made by treating the carbonate with superheated steam (steam heated to well above 100°C.). The hydroxide can be used in the refining of sugar. Sugar dissolves in water and therefore water cannot be used to wash it free of impurities. With strontium hydroxide, the sugar forms a white insoluble compound called strontium saccharate. The strontium saccharate is washed free of impurities. The sugar is reformed by blowing carbon dioxide through the saccharate. The sugar redissolves and solid particles of strontium carbonate form. They are then removed from the purified sugar. This method is not universal. Many countries use calcium hydroxide in preference to strontium hydroxide.

Because of its high oxygen content (which helps in burning) and the red colour of the flame, strontium peroxide is sometimes used in the burning mixture for tracer bullets. Strontium nitrate, though, is more popular for ordinary fireworks.

Barium compounds.

The two naturally occurring ones are barite, or barytes (barium sulphate) and witherite (barium carbonate). Unlike strontium compounds nearly all barium compounds are poisonous. Barium sulphate, a white powder, is so very insoluble that it does not have poisonous effects. In fact it is used in hospitals in the taking of X-ray photographs of the stomach and intestines. Normally the X-rays would pass straight through these parts of the body and not show up on the photograph. If the patient swallows some barium sulphate 'milk' this lines the stomach and intestines blocking the path of the X-rays and consequently a photograph is obtained.

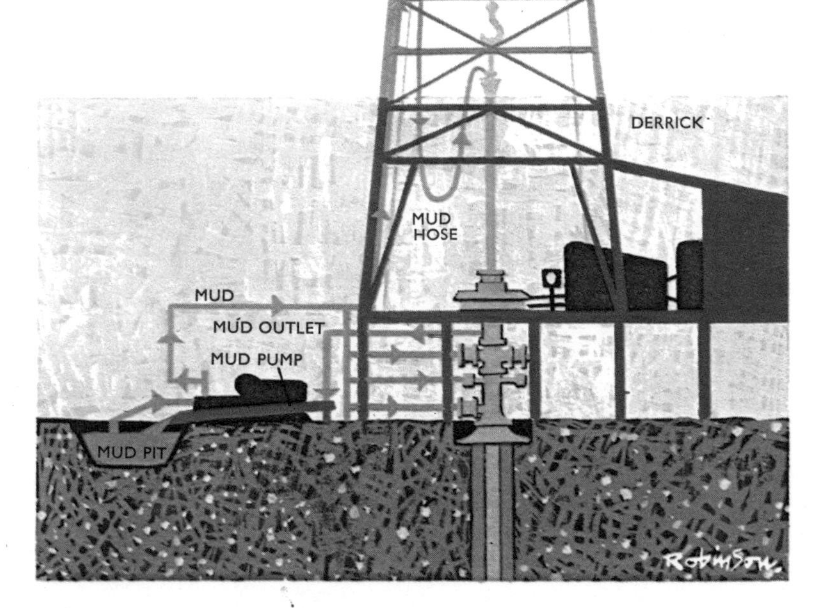

Heavy mud made of crushed barite is used to lubricate the drill during boring for oil, hold the escaping gases in check and carry rock chippings to the surface.

Barium carbonate is incorporated into the glass of television tubes to prevent X-rays produced in the tubes from getting out. Prolonged exposure to X-rays is harmful.

Quite large quantities of barium oxide are made by strongly heating barium carbonate with powdered carbon. Most of this oxide is converted into barium peroxide from which the bleach, hydrogen peroxide is made. Small quantities of the oxide are also used for the drying of gases. Barium oxide is also a most effective drying agent.

In recent years the mineral barite has become increasingly important to the petroleum industry. Like other barium compounds it is extremely heavy or dense. It is crushed and made into a heavy mud which is poured into oil wells and holds the escaping gases in check during boring. The heavy mud also lubricates the drill while the boring is taking place and brings to the surface with it rock chips from the drilling.

Barite (barium sulphate) is also the main constituent in the white pigment lithopone. Lithopone paint is not poisonous and is not blackened by hydrogen sulphide in the atmosphere as is lead paint. Lithopone is also used as a filler in rubber and linoleum.

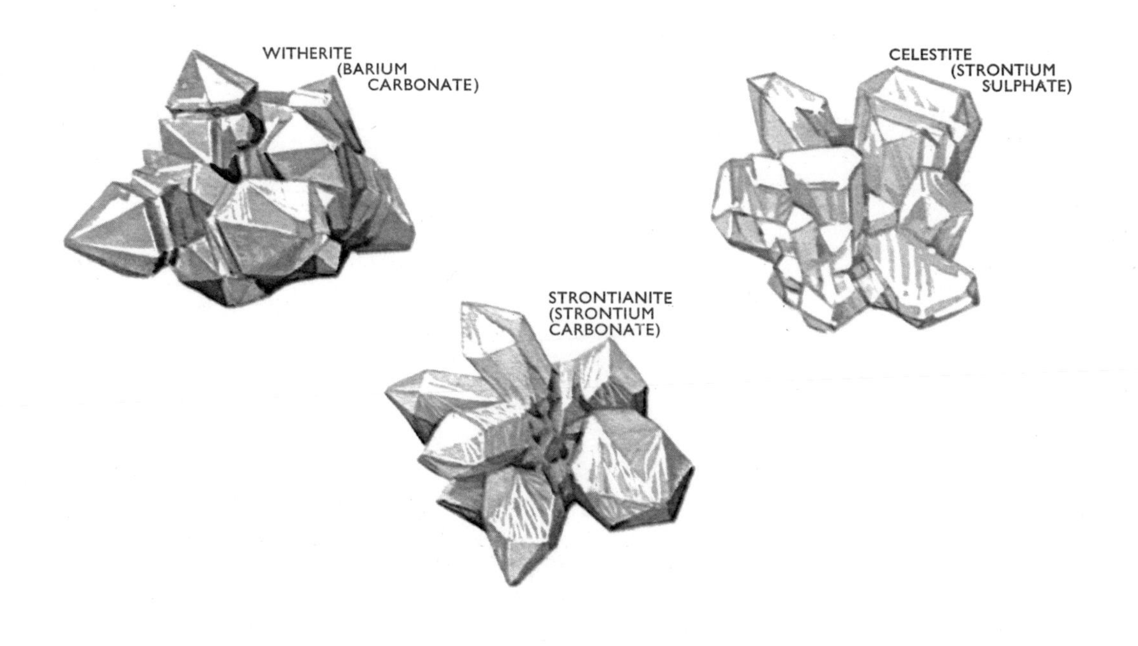

CHAPTER FIVE

Group 3

Boron

Although the element boron does not occur uncombined in Nature, some of its compounds are very familiar. Borax, for example, is a white soluble salt containing boron (in its acid radical part) used in glass-making, soldering, the pottery industry and in treating fabrics to make them fire-proof. Boric acid, a white solid which can be made from borax (although it does occur naturally in volcanic regions), is used as a mild antiseptic, sometimes under the name of boracic acid. Boron itself is added to steels to make them hard, and it is used in the control rods of some nuclear reactors.

The element can be obtained from its oxide by heating with a reducing agent such as powdered magnesium. The reaction is usually performed in a covered crucible.

$$\underset{\text{BORIC OXIDE}}{B_2O_3} + \underset{\text{MAGNESIUM}}{3Mg} \longrightarrow \underset{\text{BORON}}{2B} + \underset{\text{MAGNESIUM OXIDE}}{3MgO}$$

The element is separated from the final mixture by the action of hydrochloric acid which converts the magnesium oxide into soluble magnesium chloride. This reaction yields an impure amorphous (powder-like) form of the element. A crystalline form can be obtained by dissolving the element in molten aluminium at high temperature. Crystals separate out on cooling, but they may be an alloy of boron and aluminium.

Crystals of three boron compounds—kernite, a sodium borate mineral ($Na_2B_4O_7.4H_2O$); boric acid (H_3BO_3); and boron phosphate (BPO_4)

One of the principal world sources of borax is the opencast mine shown above. It is situated at Boron, California, and is over 300 ft. deep and 2,000 ft. long. The mineral is carried by a conveyer belt system to the processing plant in the background.

The element boron exists as brittle transparent crystals which are nearly as hard as diamond. Boron forms compounds directly with fluorine, chlorine and bromine, oxygen, sulphur and carbon. Boron carbide, which is almost as hard as diamond, is formed when boron and carbon are heated together in an electric furnace. Although the properties of boron and most of its compounds are those of a non-metal, the element is unusual in that in boron phosphate it behaves as a metal.

Boron in its elementary form is not very important commercially, but a great many uses have been found for the salts of boric acid—the borates. As already mentioned, some of the latter occur naturally, so that it is only necessary to purify these after mining. One of the world's largest deposits of borates is in California and about one million tons are obtained from that source annually. The impurities are removed by dissolving the crude borax in water, followed by filtration. Pure borax is then recovered from the clear solution by recrystallization.

If borax is heated sufficiently it melts to form a glassy substance in which metallic oxides will dissolve. The compounds which are formed by the reaction between borax and the metal oxides are sometimes highly coloured, the colour being characteristic of the metal. Thus it is possible to identify the metal present by the colour it gives to a *borax bead.* On account of the ability of metallic oxides to dissolve in molten borax, borax is used as a flux component in removing oxides from metal surfaces in preparation for soldering or welding.

Borax is used in the manufacture of boro-silicate (Pyrex) glass which has good resistance to sudden temperature changes. The principal constituents of this type of glass (from which ovenware is made) are silica (about 80%) and borax (about 12%). Borax is also used in glazing pottery and other ceramic articles, in vitreous enamel finishes for stoves, cookers and baths, and for coating paper.

Traces of boron are essential for the growth of plants. Deficiencies in the soil with respect to this, as with any other essential trace element, lead to crop yields which are poor both in quality and quantity. Such deficiencies can be corrected by the application of fertilizers which contain boron, normally in the form of soluble borates.

Aluminium

Aluminium can be separated from its ore, aluminium oxide, by electrolysis, which is the chemical decomposition of a substance by the passage of an electric current through it. The passage of an electric current through the aluminium oxide breaks it down into aluminium and oxygen.

Electrolysis would be of little value if the separated parts of a solution stayed exactly where they were liberated, rather like a mixture of sugar and salt. But they do not. When an electric current passes through water, hydrogen moves to the wire or electrode which is connected to the negative terminal of the electrical supply (the cathode), while oxygen moves to the positive electrode (the anode). In a similar way, when electrolysis takes place in aluminium oxide, the aluminium released moves to the cathode (when it can be collected), while the oxygen moves to the anode. This is the simple theory behind the refining of metals such as aluminium, though the actual process is naturally more complicated in practice.

The Production of Aluminium

Aluminium is a very abundant metal, making up almost one-tenth of the Earth's crust. As the oxide, alumina, aluminium is widely distributed in many silicate rocks and clays, but not in sufficient quantities for extraction to be economical. The chief source of the metal is bauxite, an ore with a very high alumina content (e.g. over 60%).

Bauxite compositions may vary widely according to locality but consist mainly of impure alumina, usually hydrated (combined with water) and containing iron oxides and silica as the main impurities. The first stage in the extraction is the purification of bauxite to produce a pure alumina from which the metal may be obtained directly, in a reasonable degree of purity, by electrolysis. The crushed ore is first washed (to remove clay and other foreign matter) and dried, and then further pulverised and digested under steam pressure with hot caustic soda (sodium hydroxide).

The sequence of obtaining aluminium. Mining bauxite ore (1), washing the ore (2), dissolving bauxite in hot caustic soda in steam pressure tanks (3), the precipitation tanks where aluminium hydroxide is formed (4), calcination in drums to produce alumina (5); and (right) *diagram of a furnace where the aluminium is formed by electrolysis.*

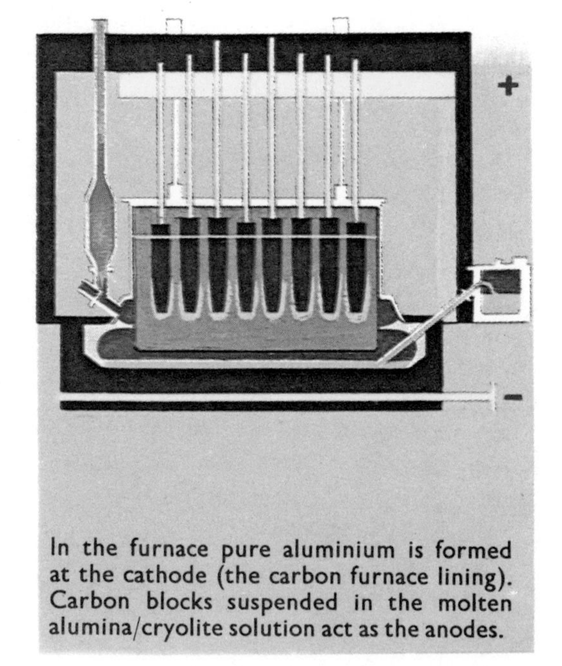

In the furnace pure aluminium is formed at the cathode (the carbon furnace lining). Carbon blocks suspended in the molten alumina/cryolite solution act as the anodes.

During this process the aluminium oxide in the bauxite is 'dissolved', and soluble sodium aluminate is formed. Other impurities in the ore, such as iron and titanium, are not dissolved and can be removed by filtering the solution.

The sodium aluminate in solution is pumped into tall 'precipitation' tanks where the hot liquid is gradually cooled. *Precipitation* is a method of taking out the dissolved solids from a solution. Hot liquids will usually allow more of a substance to be dissolved in them than when they are cold. If a hot solution is *saturated* (i.e. has as much dissolved substance in it as it will take), and if it is then cooled, it has less ability to hold the substance in solution. The excess substance which can no longer be dissolved is therefore precipitated out as a solid. This is basically what is happening to the sodium aluminate in the cooling tanks. There is however one difference, because a 'seed' of aluminium hydroxide is placed in the tanks and this hastens precipitation. The solid crystals which form from the solution are of aluminium hydroxide.

The next step is to convert this hydroxide into *alumina* (aluminium oxide). The crystals of aluminium hydroxide are heated in long revolving drums. The aim is to drive off the water which remains in the crystals, a process known as *calcination*. The result is a white powder, alumina.

The final major stage in the production of aluminium, the extraction of the aluminium from the aluminium oxide by electrolysis, is the most expensive, since it is an electrical process, demanding large supplies of power. For this reason plant refining this metal is usually situated where electricity can be obtained fairly cheaply (e.g. at Kitimat in Canada, based on the nearby Kemano hydro-electric power station). The alumina is placed in small 'furnaces' or baths (there may be as many as 1,500 of these in the plant) together with molten *cryolite*. Cryolite is another chemical compound of aluminium, though not so common as bauxite. When cryolite is molten, alumina will dissolve in it just as salt dissolves in water. The *solution* of alumina in molten cryolite will allow a current of electricity to pass through it. The 'furnace' is really a form of electrical cell, a steel bath with a carbon lining to act as a *cathode* (negative plate) and other carbon blocks in contact with the liquid to form *anodes* (the positive connection). A strong current is passed through the mixture at about 6 volts and this produces the action known as *electrolysis*, splitting up the substances electrically. The passage of current through the mixture creates great heat, keeping the temperature at about 1,000°C. Molten aluminium is deposited at the cathode at the bottom of the furnace and is drawn off from time to time. The oxygen which is liberated during electrolysis rises to come in contact with the red-hot carbon anodes, to form carbon monoxide. This gas burns at the surface to form carbon dioxide which is led away as fumes. Although in theory only the alumina is used up during the process, in fact a certain amount of cryolite is also involved and has to be replaced. The amount of electricity consumed is enormous. One could burn a two-bar electric fire for 1,000 hours on the same quantity of electricity as is used to produce a single ton of aluminium.

Aluminium is light and fairly strong, particularly when alloyed with other metals. It is used in making aircraft equipment, kitchen utensils and for many kinds of transport and other engineering machinery. The use of aluminium in the superstructure of one ship, for instance, produced such a saving in weight, compared with steel, that it allowed an extra deck to be incorporated. Aluminium is a good conductor of electricity when in a pure form and for this reason is often employed in overhead wiring (usually around a steel core). Because it does not rust, aluminium has been found useful in the building industry for roofs, window frames and many other fittings.

The metals sodium, potassium, calcium, strontium, barium, cadmium, chromium, zinc and magnesium can all be separated from their ores industrially by electrolysis. Crude copper, tin, nickel and cobalt can be purified by electrolysis. In each case the metal is attracted to the negative cathode and deposited there.

Extracting molten aluminium from the furnaces (cells) where it has been obtained by the electrolysis of alumina. Later the aluminium is collected in holding furnaces and then cast into ingots.

CHAPTER SIX

The Transition Elements

THE 'octave' classification with the number of electrons increasing until the 'magic number' of eight electrons is achieved works very well for the elements of small atomic weight, but it falls down in the fourth period of elements. In the earlier periods there is the expected build up of electrons in the outer shell, from one to eight, but in the fourth period this pattern is interrupted. The first element, potassium, has a single outer shell electron. The second element, calcium, has two electrons. The third element, scandium, would be expected to have three electrons but, in fact, has only two. Most of the next nine elements in the third period have only two electrons in the outer N shell. The atoms of the elements have extra electrons but instead of going to the outer shell they are going to the next inner M shell. So scandium has only two electrons in the N shell, but has nine in its M shell. Its neighbour titanium has ten electrons in its M shell, and the build-up of electrons in the M shell continues until zinc is reached. This has eighteen electrons in its inner M shell. After zinc, the original pattern with the build-up of the outer N shell of electrons is continued. The last elements of the period all have eighteen electrons in the M shell and they progress, one electron at a time until eight electrons are acquired by the outer N shell.

All the elements from scandium to zinc are called *transition elements*. In the fifth and sixth periods of the periodic table the build-up of the outer shell is similarly interrupted. Further families of transition elements are formed by the build-up of electrons in inner shells in these periods. The outer shells contain only two electrons and the elements have many properties in common.

Properties of the Transition Elements

Many of the most common and important metals are transition elements, including iron, copper, zinc, silver and gold. All of the transition elements are dense shiny metals – good conductors of heat and electricity. Included in the transition metals are the strongly magnetic (*ferromagnetic*)

Most salts of the transition metals have distinctive colours. This also applies to the complex ions that the metals form. Copper forms the complex ion $Cu(NH_3)_4$ when ammonium hydroxide solution is added to a solution of copper salt.

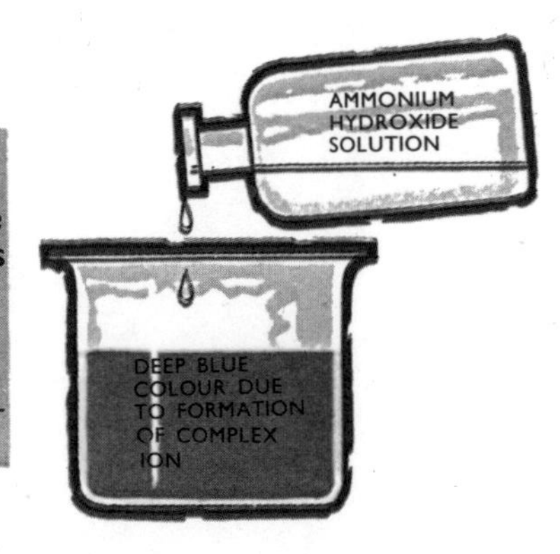

LETTERS K, L, M, N, REFER TO ELECTRON SHELLS, AND NUMBERS REFER TO NUMBERS OF ELECTRONS IN THOSE SHELLS
H
K
1
He
K
2
FIRST PERIOD
Li K L 2 1
Be K L 2 2
B K L 2 3
K L 2 4
N K L 2 5
O K L 2 6
F K L 2 7
Ne K L 2 8
SECOND PERIOD
EXTRA ELECTRONS PASS TO OUTER (L) SHELL
Na K L M 2 8 1
Mg K L M 2 8 2
Al K L M 2 8 3
Si K L M 2 8 4
P K L M 2 8 5
S K L M 2 8 6
Cl K L M 2 8 7
Ar K L M 2 8 8
THIRD PERIOD
K K L M N 2 8 8 1
Ca K L M N 2 8 8 2
Ga K L M N 2 8 18 3
Ge K L M N 2 8 18 4
As K L M N 2 8 18 5
Se K L M N 2 8 18 6
Br K L M N 2 8 18 7
Kr K L M N 2 8 18 8
FOURTH PERIOD
SCANDIUM
IN BUILD-UP OF ELECTRON SHELLS IN TRANSITION ELEMENTS ELECTRONS ARE ADDED TO INNER SHELL
K L M N
POTASSIUM
CALCIUM
IN 'BUILD-UP' OF ELECTRON SHELLS ELECTRONS ARE NORMALLY ADDED TO OUTER SHELL
Sc K L M N 2 8 9 2
Ti K L M N 2 8 10 2
V K L M N 2 8 11 2
Cr K L M N 2 8 13 1
Mn K L M N 2 8 13 2
Fe K L M N 2 8 14 2
Co K L M N 2 8 15 2
Ni K L M N 2 8 16 2
Cu K L M N 2 8 18 1
THE FIRST GROUP OF TRANSITION ELEMENTS BREAKS INTO THE FOURTH PERIOD BETWEEN CALCIUM AND GALLIUM

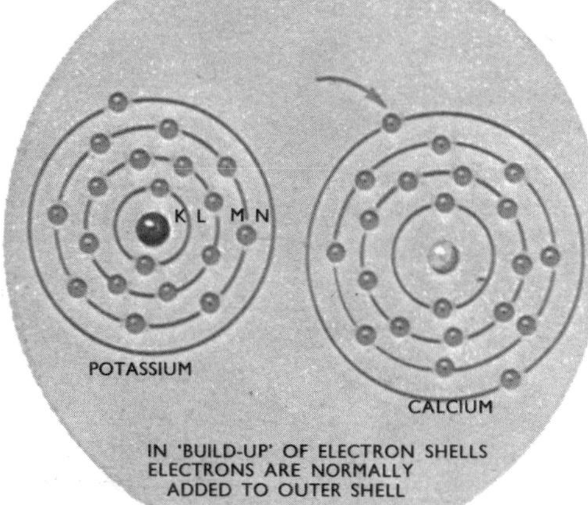

The first part of the periodic table, showing the intervention of the first family of transition elements into the fourth period. The electrons are gained by an inner shell, and not the outer shell, as expected.

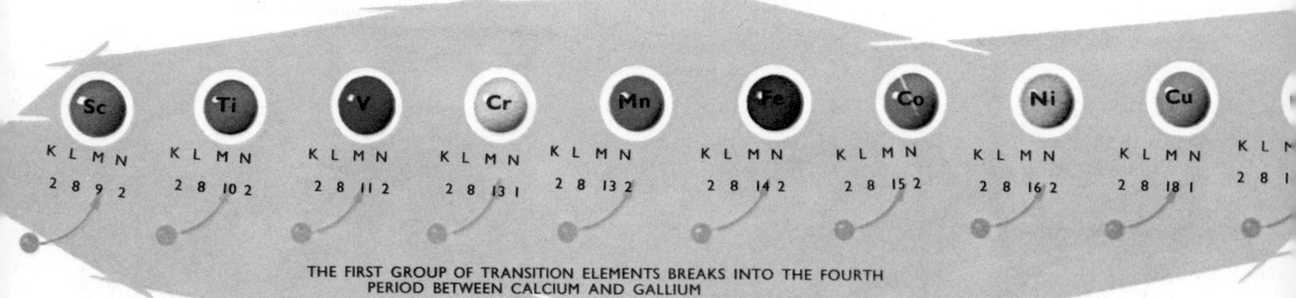

metals iron, cobalt and nickel. Most of the other transition metals are paramagnetic – weak versions of the ferromagnetic materials. These magnetic properties are due, once again, to the arrangements of electrons in the shells. In ferromagnetic materials, for example, there are *unpaired* electrons in the shells – for one electron spinning in one direction there is not another spinning in the opposite direction to neutralize the magnetic effects produced by the first.

The chemical properties of these metals are very largely affected by the tendency of the electrons in the inner shell to take part in chemical bondings. Apparently, there is an 'urge' on the part of these electrons to behave in a similar way to the valence electrons in the outer shell. They are similar in behaviour to the electrons in the outer shell because they, too, are not occupying a complete shell of electrons. For example, an atom of the transition element iron may lose two electrons from its outer shell to form the ion Fe^{++}, or, in addition, lose a third electron from the next shell to form the ion Fe^{+++}.

The main factor in determining the chemical properties of these elements is, however, the electrons in the outer shell, and in passing along the period from one element to the next the properties of neighbouring transitional elements change very little.

The transitional elements all form positive ions, usually highly coloured both in the solid and in solution. Some of them also form *complex ions*. The metallic ion takes up molecules of water or ammonia, or even other ions and chemical groups (e.g. the cyanide ion CN^-) to form these *coordination* compounds. A well known example of this is the cuprammonium ion $Cu(NH_3)_4^{2+}$ formed when ammonia solution is added to a solution of a copper salt. The deep-blue solution that results is used to confirm the presence of copper ions in qualitative analysis.

Titanium

Although the metal titanium is the fourth most abundant metal in the Earth's crust, it was the development of the aircraft industry that first thrust it into a position of importance.

When first discovered over 150 years ago, it was a problem element which for years puzzled and defeated metallurgists. They did their utmost to extract it economically and make something useful out of it. In fact, the metal was so difficult to extract from its ores that it was not until 1949 that an economical method was found.

There are two main titanium ores, *rutile*, an impure form of titanium dioxide, and *ilmenite*, a mixture of oxides of titanium and iron. All the titanium metal is obtained from rutile while titanium compounds are manufactured from ilmenite.

The method worked out for titanium metal in 1949 by the American W. J. Kroll involved converting the titanium in the ore into titanium tetrachloride $TiCl_4$. This is then reduced to the metal by reacting this compound with magnesium. The metal produced looked rather like spongy cobbles of coke.

The Kroll process is still widely used in America and Japan, but a

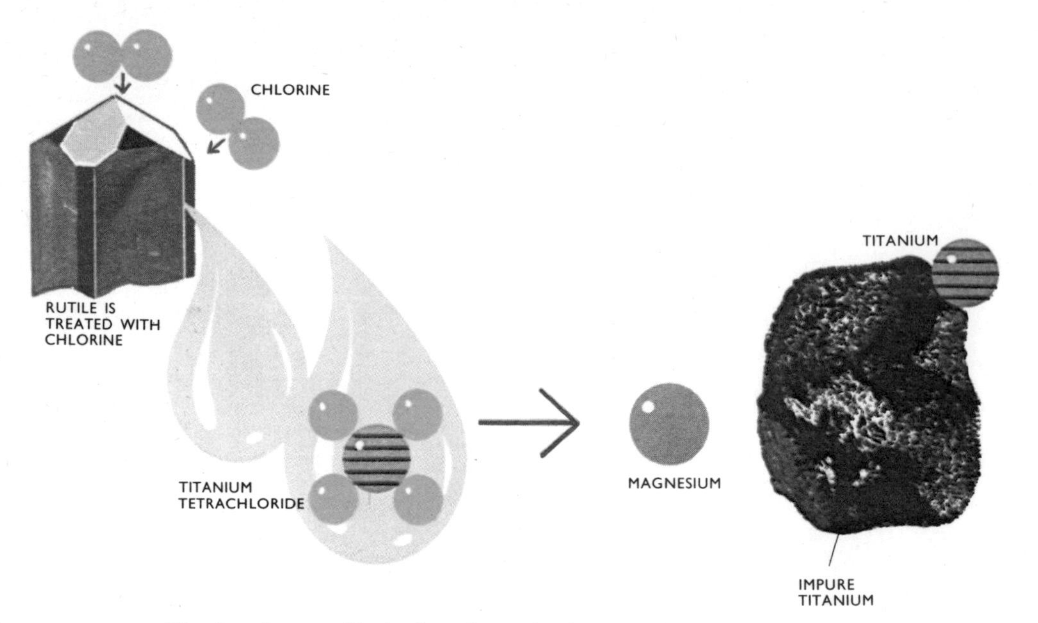

To prepare metallic titanium, rutile is first heated with chlorine in the presence of carbon to form titanium tetrachloride. This is then reduced to the metal by heating with magnesium.

different chemical method, involving large quantities of sodium, is now used in England, producing dull grey metallic granules instead.

In its spongy and granular form the metal is of little use and must be consolidated and have air bubbles and flaws driven out before it can be called useful. This cannot be done by melting and pouring into a cast. Titanium melts at nearly 1700°C, 200° higher than the melting point of steel. At that temperature it would react with the lining of the furnace and absorb gases from the air to make it useless as a structural metal.

Granules of raw metallic titanium, sometimes mixed with other powdered metals to make alloys, are thoroughly blended and fed into a 2500-ton press which squares the powder into a briquette. The briquettes are then welded together to make an electrode 12 feet long and weighing almost a ton.

The electrode is suspended from the top of the furnace while a water-cooled crucible is clamped on at the bottom. Air is drawn out, an arc is struck between the electrode and a small quantity of titanium powder in the crucible base. The electrode slowly melts to form an ingot. The melting is repeated with the whole operation handled by remote control.

High frequency sound waves (ultrasonic waves) are used to test for flaws. This is an echo sounding technique. Flaws inside the metal act as mirrors for the beam, preventing it from passing through the metal. No signal on the far side indicates a flaw.

Aircraft Engineering

The aircraft industry requires lightweight alloys which can withstand the stresses imposed by ultra-high-speed flight and titanium provides the answer. Its density is only 60% of the density of steel while it keeps its strength at temperatures far higher than those considered safe for aluminium alloys, the other lightweight alternative.

The aircraft industry uses titanium for its turbine compressor blades, exhaust shrouds and hot air ducts, also on the leading edges of the wings where it can resist erosion from the air rushing past.

Because of its high resistance to corrosion by acids etc., the metal is also being used for manufacturing corrosion-free vessels and pipes for the chemical industry.

On a much smaller scale, but for the same reason, surgical implements such as internal splints and screws used for fixing bones together, clips and surgical nails made of titanium are gradually taking over from stainless steel.

Radiation Shielding

Nuclear power stations use titanium for many of their internal components because of the ability of the metal and its alloys to shield radiation. The irradiated metal quickly loses any radioactivity, making the parts easy to handle and easing the maintenance of the reactor.

White Pigment

Many white paints and inks owe their whiteness to the pigment, titanium dioxide, TiO_2, the only compound of titanium of any real importance. White plastic floor coverings and white rubber are white in colour because this compound is incorporated in them. Textiles can be sprayed with it to counteract unwanted lustre and enamels and tile glazes can be treated with it to regulate the colour, opacity and gloss.

After being compressed to form a huge electrode, the titanium is loaded into a crucible. The crucible has its air withdrawn and the electrode slowly melts and consolidates.

Titanium as a Transition Metal

As we proceed from left to right in the periodic table, the elements gain an extra electron, one at a time, in their outer shells to build a stable octet of eight electrons. But electrons are sometimes added to an inner shell, which might reach 18 or 32 electrons. Titanium is one of a group of elements – the *transition* group. These all have two electrons in the outer shell but the inner shell has between 9 electrons and 18 electrons.

There are two different ways in which titanium oxide is used by the paper industry. It can be incorporated during the making and its particles held throughout the body of the sheet to reflect the light and make the paper appear whiter, or it can be painted on as a surface coating. It is usual to coat the thicker papers with the oxide, but for airmail paper where it must be flimsy but not transparent, the oxide pigment is spread through the paper pulp during the making. White waxed wrapping paper is only white because of the titanium oxide added to it.

The extraction of the metal titanium and the manufacture of its pigment oxide are quite independent processes. The pigment is not made from the metal, but also has its starting point in the titanium ore ilmenite.

The pigment is made from ilmenite by crushing the ore and dissolving out the titanium with concentrated sulphuric acid. When the solution has been boiled down and cooled, the iron that also dissolved crystallizes out and can be separated. Concentrating the liquid even further brings out the titanium as hydrated crystals of titanium sulphate.

These crystals are filtered out and washed before being fed into a rotary furnace where sulphurous gases are driven off, leaving impure particles of titanium dioxide behind. After purification and grinding to the right size they are ready to be mixed with paper pulp or paint.

Titanium is used by the aircraft industry because of its strength, resistance to corrosion and light weight. Its properties make titanium ideal for the firewalls on the engine bays of modern jet aircraft.

In our modern civilization tungsten has become a vitally important metal, despite the relatively small annual production which is only 17 times that of gold.

Most metals were in use centuries ago but tungsten is an exception in that it has no ancient and historic past. The ancient Egyptians did not use it, neither did the Romans. In fact, the metal was only first isolated from a sample of ore in 1783 and even then, it took World War I to find a use for it. Although its possibilities as a hardener of metals had been pointed out only a few years after its isolation, it was first put into practical use in German munitions factories just before 1914 to make high speed cutting tools. Ironically, most of the tungsten for these tools came from the English mines in Cornwall. It was sold cheaply to the Germans because the English could find no use for it, and they had no idea that they were responsible for the enormous production of German guns.

Later on when its value in tool-steel making became general knowledge, the price soared and tungsten joined the ranks of the more highly-priced metals.

Tungsten has the distinction of being the metal with the highest melting point – about 3,410°C. This is why it was only recently isolated. Whereas most metals can be melted and the impurities skimmed off as a slag, the high melting point of tungsten renders this impossible, and purely chemical methods have to be used instead.

The largest tungsten deposits are found in China and Burma followed by North America and the Andes of South America. There are also quite a few smaller deposits in other countries. Although the composition of the ore varies from mine to mine, the ores fall into two categories. The *wolframite* ores contain iron and manganese tungstate, $FeWO_4$ and $MnWO_4$. (W is the chemical symbol of tungsten). The other group, the *scheelite* ores contain calcium tungstate $CaWO_4$.

At the mines, the useful part of the ore is concentrated by a series of processes which may include crushing and flotation. Magnetic separation is also used for wolframite because the ore can be picked out with a magnet leaving the unwanted part behind. The exact procedure depends very much on the nature of the ore, but on the whole it is similar to the concentra-

The two main ores of tungsten, wolframite and scheelite.

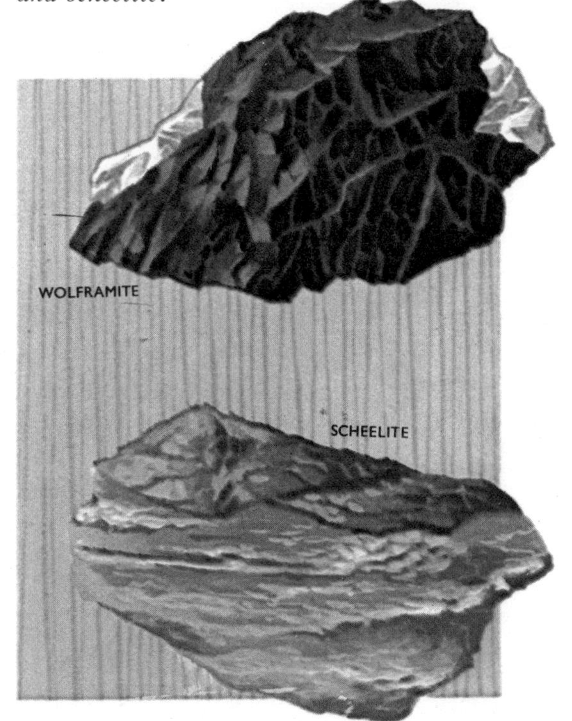

Reduction furnaces in which hydrogen reduces tungstic acid to fine particles of tungsten metal.

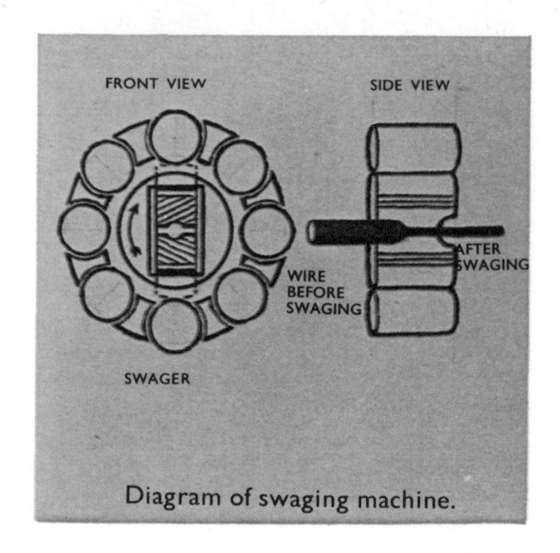

Diagram of swaging machine.

tion of many other metal ores.

Then comes the difference. Instead of smelting, *tungstic acid* is obtained from the ore and then the acid is reduced to give granules of metallic tungsten.

Extraction

The concentrate is heated at about 800°–900°C. to drive off any sulphur and arsenic as gases. Afterwards it is mixed with sodium carbonate and converted into fine particles. The mixture is roasted in a furnace with a plentiful supply of air to oxidize the iron and manganese content of wolframite or the calcium content of scheelite. Sodium tungstate Na_2WO_4 is formed and the other metals form oxides. The metallic oxides are insoluble in water but the sodium tungstate, like all other sodium salts, is soluble in water and this is the key to its extraction. The rocky material is shaken with hot water for several hours and the part which has not dissolved is filtered off. The filtrate is a solution of crude sodium tungstate.

Part of the water is evaporated off to reduce its bulk and then the solution is cooled. More impurities separate out and are removed. The rest of the water is then driven off leaving behind crystals of sodium tungstate. The crystals are redissolved and the solution is further purified by precipitating out more impurities. Hydrochloric acid is used to bring down from the solution a yellow precipitate of tungstic acid.

$$\underset{\text{sodium tungstate}}{Na_2WO_4} + \underset{\text{hydrochloric acid}}{2HCl} \rightarrow \underset{\text{tungstic acid}}{H_2WO_4} + \underset{\text{sodium chloride}}{2NaCl}$$

Tungsten metal powder is obtained from this yellow tungstic acid in reduction furnaces where hydrogen is pumped in to act as a reducing agent and sweep away the waste products, leaving behind fine particles of metallic tungsten.

Articles of pure tungsten are made by applying pressure to the powder and squashing the article into shape in

Swaging tungsten wire. The wire is hammered to make it less brittle and reduce its diameter.

Carburizing furnaces in which tungsten carbide is made by heating tungsten powder with powdered carbon.

These cutting edges and wear-resisting parts are made from tungsten carbide.

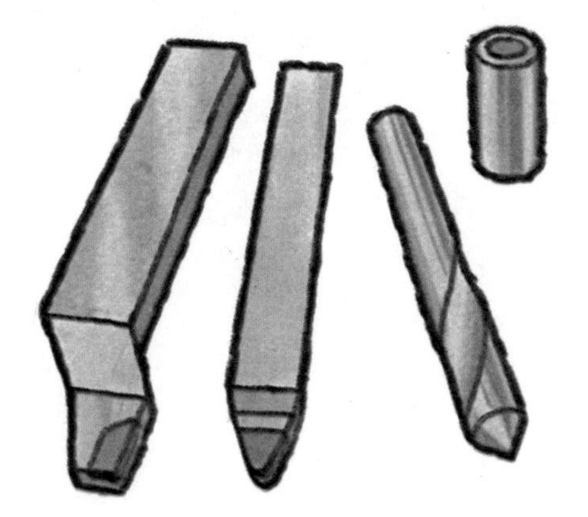

this way. After this treatment the metal is rather brittle, but further mechanical treatment such as pounding with a hammer soon gives increased toughness to the tungsten.

Uses

Tungsten, the element is used to make the filament of electric light bulbs. With its exceptionally high melting point there is little chance of the metal evaporating off and so the filament has a fairly long life. Because it remains unchanged at high temperatures it is an excellent metal for the heating filaments of high temperature furnaces and also for the nozzles of rockets. Contact points in spark plugs and X-ray targets are also made of tungsten. Alloyed with other metals, it makes hard steel cutting tools which will still be hard even at high temperatures.

Tungsten carbide (WC), is the best known compound of tungsten. It is obtained by heating a mixture of metal powder and powdered carbon in a furnace. Many cutting blades which must preserve their sharpness even after cutting large quantities of tough material have a coating of tungsten carbide. This material is noted for its resistance to wear and apart from cutting also finds use in polishing the rough edges off other metal objects. Some compounds of tungsten are also used as mordants in dyeing. These enable the dye to 'take' on the material. Other compounds can also be used because of their value as a pigment, giving a peach-coloured tint to pottery.

When iron is exposed to the oxygen of the air and to water, it falls away to rust. The iron, in fact, reverts back to the oxide from which it was extracted. Many iron ores are brick red and resemble rust in appearance. Others are yellow or purple. They may be powdery or rock hard. The most common ore is *haematite* which contains ferric oxide (Fe_2O_3). A high grade ore contains about 65% iron. Russia is the largest producer, making 116 million tons annually, while France and Luxemburg together make 73 million tons. Sometimes the ore is mined deep within the ground and in other places it is simply scooped from the surface with huge mechanical shovels.

But whatever the source of the ore, it undergoes a routine analysis and is then stored in batches according to grade. It is most important to know the iron content (so that the final amount of iron can be calculated) and also the type and quantity of the impurities. (Some impurities may be removed by pre-roasting.)

The Blast Furnace

Coke is the form of carbon used in the blast furnace. It is made by strongly heating a special grade of coking coal. Three tons of coal are needed to produce two tons of coke. The special qualities of coking coal are that it leaves very little ash and the coke made from it is strong and does not collapse under the great weight of the other substances in the furnace.

Limestone is the third substance used in the production of iron. It combines with the unwanted earthy part of the ore to form a glass-like substance, *slag*, which can easily be run off from the furnace.

A modern blast furnace is a huge hundred foot high steel cylinder lined with brick and shaped rather like the chimney of an old oil lamp.

The output from a modern furnace can be 15,000 tons or more of iron every 24 hours. The process is a continuous one and the furnaces run day and night non-stop for a period of 5 years, after which time they are dismantled to be given new refractory linings of firebricks.

At ground level near the furnace are hoppers in which the furnace charge of coke, limestone, iron ore and sinter is stored. The three hoppers deliver their contents down a single chute, first a certain quantity of coke, then iron ore and then limestone. A

General view of an ironworks showing two blast furnaces, and in the foreground, the hot air stove.

conveyor belt carries the charge to the top of the furnace. There it is relatively cool (200°C), but the heat increases further down. At the bottom the temperature is around 1,700°C. Hot air between 500°C and 1,000°C is blown in here. In some instances the output of a furnace may be increased by blowing in oil with the air and adding oxygen to the air supply. The daily intake of a blast furnace producing 1,500 tons of iron is about 2,500 tons of ore, 1,000 tons of coke, 250 tons of limestone and 4,000 tons of air.

The preheated air rushes in through openings known as *tuyeres* situated around the bottom of the furnace. The hot air burns the coke forming carbon dioxide gas.

$$\underset{\text{carbon}}{C} + \underset{\text{oxygen}}{O_2} \rightarrow \underset{\text{carbon dioxide}}{CO_2} + \text{heat}$$

This is an *exothermic* chemical reaction. Great heat is given out by the burning and as a result the temperature rises. At this high temperature carbon dioxide is immediately reduced by more coke to carbon monoxide gas.

$$\underset{\text{carbon dioxide}}{CO_2} + \underset{\text{carbon}}{C} \rightarrow \underset{\text{carbon monoxide}}{2CO}$$

Molecules of carbon monoxide can take up further atoms of oxygen to once more become carbon dioxide and do this by robbing the iron ore of its oxygen so that the oxide is reduced to

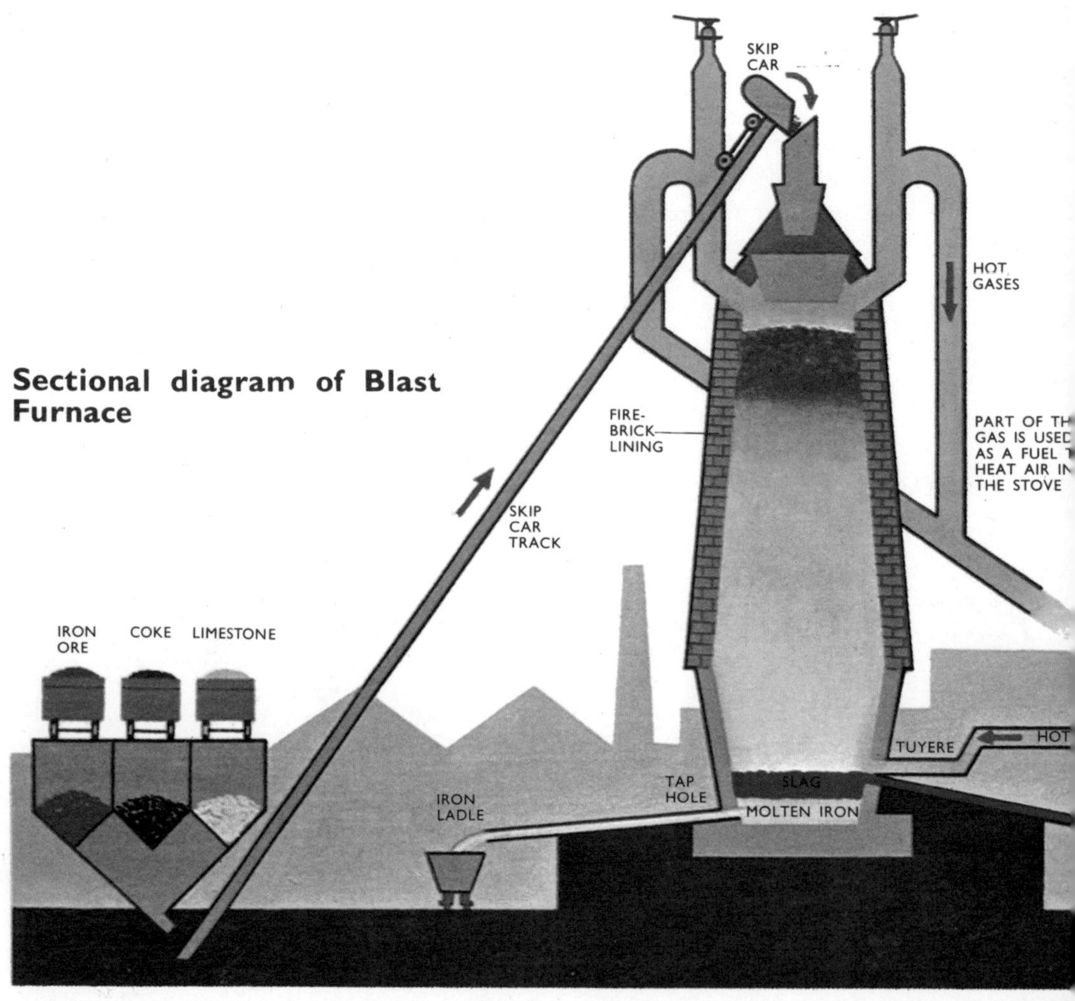

Sectional diagram of Blast Furnace

metallic iron. This is actually brought about by a complicated series of chemical reactions, but the total result can be represented by one equation:—

$$Fe_2O_3 + 3CO \rightarrow 2Fe + 3CO_2$$

ferric oxide, carbon monoxide, iron, carbon dioxide

The iron formed in this inferno is molten and trickles down to the bottom of the furnace where a pool of it collects. Situated around this part of the furnace are clay stoppered tap holes which in a modern furnace are opened once every 4 or 5 hours to let some 300–400 tons of molten iron gurgle out into giant ladles.

This iron contains a little carbon taken from the coke. Most of the earthy impurities in the ore have been taken up by the limestone. The molten limestone combines with them to form slag which also trickles down towards the bottom of the furnace. As molten slag is not as dense as molten iron it floats on top of it and like the iron is drawn off from time to time, from another tap hole higher up the furnace than the one through which the iron flows. The slag used to be wasted but now some is solidified and broken up for road making, some foamed to make a type of brick and some employed in cement making.

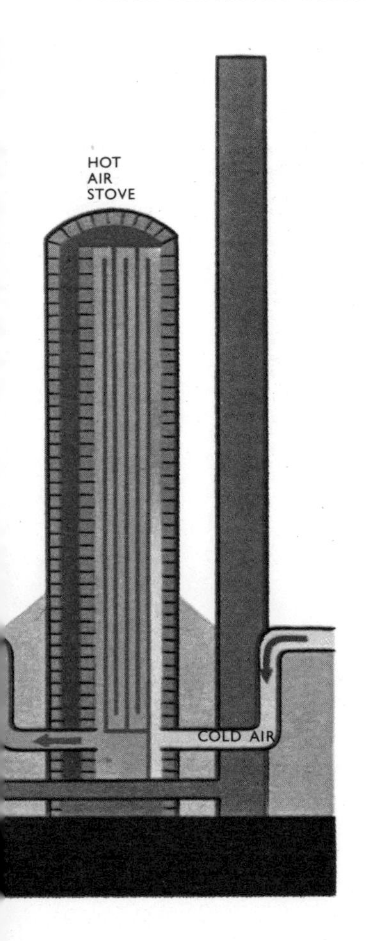

When iron comes from the blast furnace, where it has been extracted from its ore, it is a relatively useless material, for although it is strong, it is also very brittle and tends to break and crack when placed under strain. This iron is known as *cast iron* or *pig iron* because of the pig-shaped slabs in which it used to be cast. While it is in the blast furnace, pig iron takes from 2 to 5% of carbon into its structure. The carbon is taken up from the coke used in extracting the iron from its ore and is mainly responsible for its brittleness and rigidity. If all the carbon is removed, the effect is just as bad. The iron loses its brittleness and becomes very pliable, it also loses its strength and bends far too easily for most purposes.

To get the springiness of steel together with its great strength, the carbon content must be very carefully regulated. Steels contain from 0·05 to 1·5% of carbon depending on the type of steel. Other metals are often added to make special types of steel. For example, chromium and nickel are added to make *stainless steel.* Small quantities of tungsten can be added to give increased strength.

Although steel has been in use since the Middle Ages, large scale production has only come into being over the last century. Before then it was a very

Slag which contains the impurities and floats on top of the molten iron being drawn off into a large slag ladle.

An oxygen lance being used to open a tap hole in a blast furnace.

Every four or five hours molten iron is drawn off. The hot metal flows through these channels into the giant ladles.

expensive commodity tediously made in small quantities by hammering molten iron to squeeze out the slag. The slag took the carbon with it. A little carbon was put back by heating the iron with wood.

Then in 1855 Henry Bessemer in England found that if a blast of cold air was blown through molten iron, the carbon and other impurities were rapidly oxidized and blown away as gases. He patented his Bessemer converter for doing this on a large scale. Many Bessemer converters now operate using a blast of pure oxygen and steam instead of air, which speeds up the process considerably. Large quantities of steel are also made by the *open hearth* process, in which oxygen or air is blown over a shallow heated hearth containing impure molten iron. In both processes, the impurities are burnt out of the molten metal.

Nickel

Long ago when the Saxon miners stumbled upon nickel ore, they mistakenly thought it to be that of copper and were disgusted with the hard white useless metal they got from it. It was far too hard to hammer into shape and they could do nothing with it. Old Nick, the devil, had put a curse on the mine and the metal came to be called *nickel*.

The curse has long since lifted, for nickel is now a valuable commodity with an annual world production of approximately 280,000 tons. About one third of this is used in making stainless steels. It also finds use in many other alloys because of the strength and toughness, heat and corrosion resistance which it imparts to them. Some of these, the cupronickels, alloys of copper and nickel, are used in the condenser tubes of ships because of their resistance to corrosion by sea water. Exhaust steam is condensed in these tubes before being returned to the boilers. Nickel plating is also of great importance. Here, a protective layer of nickel acts as an undercoat for the very thin outer cover of chromium.

Much of the nickel produced in the world comes from the vast mines of Sudbury in Canada. The nickel is never found alone. It is far too

Enlarged cross section of a piece of Sudbury ore. The 14 elements marked on the periodic table are all found in the ore.

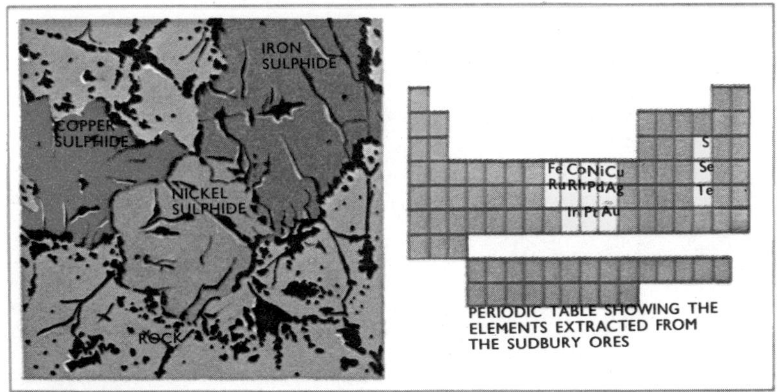

The cascading 4-inch diameter rods in this rod mill grind the crushed ore to a pulp.

Separation of the ore by flotation. Some crystals sink and some rise to the top in a froth of bubbles.

sociable and always has a crowd of other elements living with it. Most of these are neighbours on the periodic table. Apart from nickel, a piece of Sudbury ore contains other metals, notably copper and iron with small traces of platinum, silver and gold.

The ore is not an even mixture of all these substances, but consists of crystals of impure nickel sulphide, iron sulphide and copper sulphide embedded in rock. When the ore is crushed, it shatters at the boundaries between crystals, and the crystals separate, one from another.

The first stage in separating the nickel from the rest is mechanical. The ore is crushed, mixed with water and bombarded by tumbling metal rods in a rod mill until it is a fine grit. Later, in a ball mill, it is bombarded to a fine slurry. The slurry is now a mixture of different types of crystal.

The tiny crystals are separated into fractions by flotation. Certain chemicals are added to water to make it froth more easily and to make the nickel and copper sulphides attractive to air bubbles and the iron sulphide repulsive to them. When air is blown in at the bottom of the tanks the copper and nickel sulphides rise to the top in a froth of glistening bubbles and the iron sulphide sinks. After skimming off, the copper ore is further separated from the nickel ore again by flotation, only this time different chemicals are used so that the nickel sinks and the copper rises. The separated ore goes to settling tanks where it collects as a sludge at the bottom of the tanks. A vacuum filter finally removes the water from the sludge, completing the initial separation.

To obtain pure nickel, the sulphur must be removed and also any remaining copper, iron and rock still contaminating it.

As it is impossible to remove the sulphur all at once, it is removed in

Enlargement of a cross-section of a piece of ingot.

Matte from the converter is slowly cooled in moulds to form ingots.

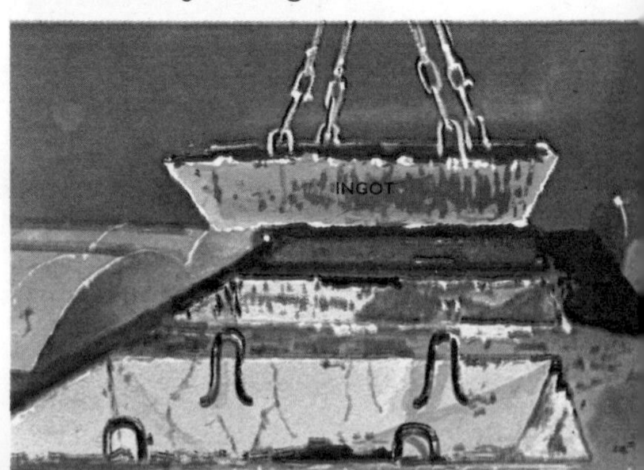

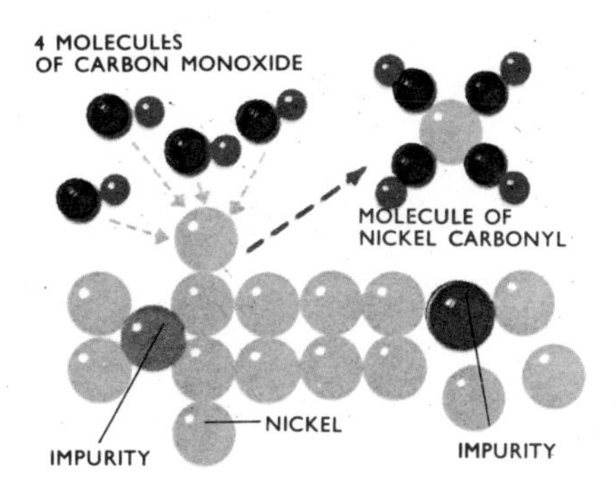

Volatilizers in which nickel is carried off by carbon monoxide as nickel carbonyl gas. The impurities in the nickel are left behind.

several carefully regulated steps taking out a little at a time.

First the ore concentrate is mixed with special grade sand and roasted in a *multiple-hearth furnace*. This consists of several compartments one above another, each one hotter than the one above. The charge moves slowly down the furnace and when it grows hot enough it ignites. The sulphur combines with the iron and burns off as sulphur dioxide, leaving iron oxide behind. The charge is removed before very much of the sulphur combined with the nickel has a chance to burn off. As iron oxide can be removed as a slag, this has paved the way for the removal of the iron in the next stage.

The Extraction of Nickel from its Ore

The majority of iron oxide is removed in a *reverbatory furnace*. The glowing mass from the hearth is heated by burning gusts of powdered coal. The temperature rises as the heat rebounds from the walls and is not allowed to escape. The charge metals and the iron oxide forms a slag with the molten sand. The slag is not very dense and floats to the top in the same way that oil floats on water, so it can be separated by tapping off. Then the *matte* of molten nickel and sulphur can also be run off.

Huge ladles carry the molten matte to *converters* where the sulphur is driven off as sulphur dioxide and the remaining iron is removed in a slag. Quartz sand is added. The converting process is somewhat like the Bessemer process used in steelmaking. Cold air under low pressure is blown in at the side of the cylinder-shaped vessel and rushes and roars its way up through the molten matte, oxidising sulphur to sulphur dioxide and metallic iron to iron oxides, while the converter spits forth showers of flames. The 'blow' is allowed to continue until there is not quite enough sulphur present to combine with all the nickel and copper. The air supply is stopped and the converter is tilted to first pour off the slag and then the matte.

The liquid matte is poured into cooling moulds lined with insulating bricks and then covered with insulating lids. In these moulds the cooling is very slow indeed. Crystals of copper sulphide form and grow, then crystals of an alloy of copper and nickel, because locally there was not enough sulphur present to combine with all the metal.

Finally, nickel sulphide crystals grow. The cooling is kept slow to give the various parts of the matte

-E

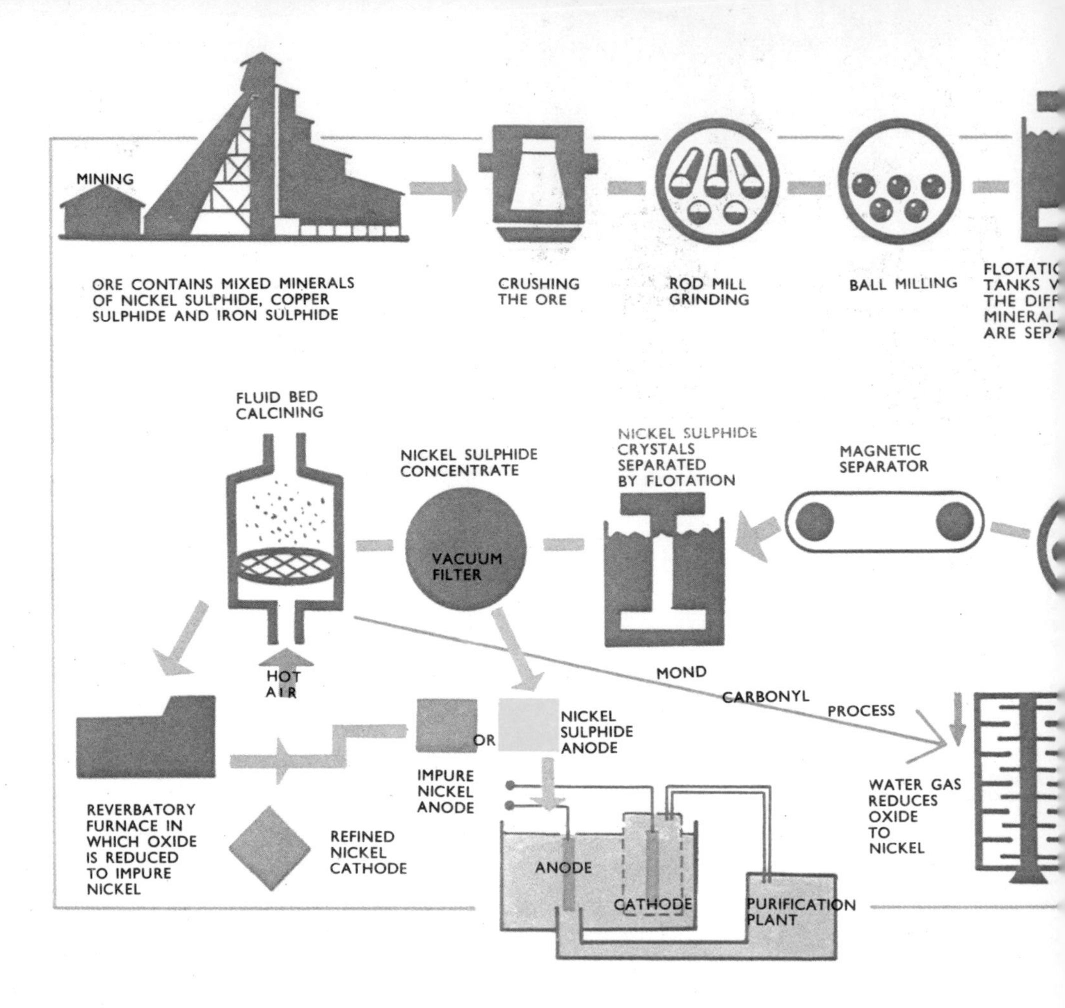

time to separate completely.

When an ingot has formed it will shatter at the boundaries between the various crystals, enabling the different crystals to be separated in a similar fashion to the first stage of the extraction. The ingots are passed through crushers, and rod and ball mills reduce them to a slurry. The crystals of alloy are magnetic and are separated out using a magnetic belt conveyor. Just as before, the two remaining types of crystal are separated by flotation. Then, the small amount of copper-nickel alloy with its charge of precious metals goes to the precious metal refinery, and the copper sulphide to the copper plant.

The impure nickel concentrate has its sulphur finally removed by a *fluid bed calcining* process. In this a layer of sulphide about four feet thick is placed on a fine grid at the bottom of a cylindrical column. Hot air is blown up through the grid, lifting the bed of sulphide until it is a fluid mass supported by the rising air. At this stage the bed is about twelve feet deep. Each of the particles is completely separated from its neighbours and is rapidly converted to oxide by the surrounding hot air, the process generating its own heat. The sulphur is carried off as sulphur dioxide, and the particles become *nickel oxide calcine.*

Some of this calcine is used for making steels and other alloys but most of it is transported away from the mines for refining into very pure nickel.

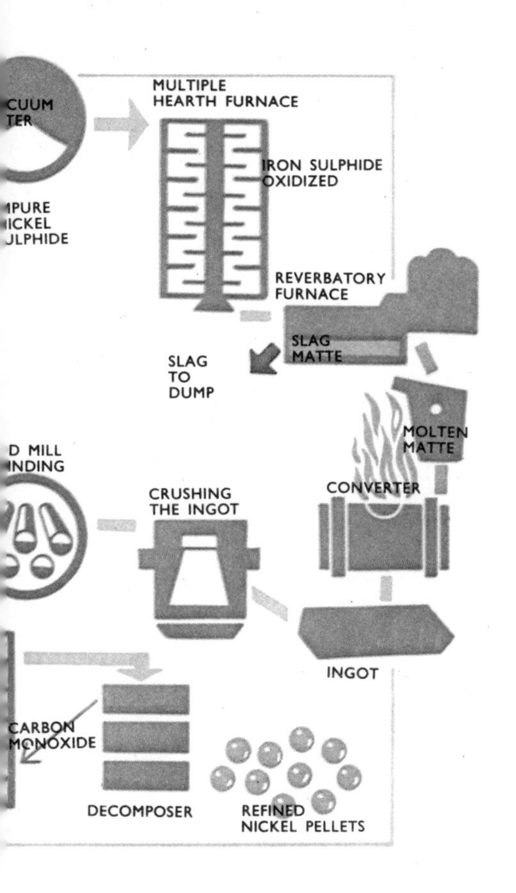

There are two alternative methods of doing this. Where there is a plentiful supply of cheap electricity, electrolysis is preferred. The other method is the *nickel carbonyl process.*

Electrolytic Refining

The starting material is sometimes nickel oxide calcine which is reduced in a furnace to crude metallic nickel and then cast into anode shapes. But the latest method uses the nickel sulphide from the slow cooling and flotation process as its starting material. The nickel sulphide is melted and cast directly into a sulphide anode shape, so avoiding the calcining and reduction processes.

The anodes (either sulphide or metallic anodes) are connected to a generator of direct current; so are the thin pure nickel cathodes. They are placed alternately in a solution of nickel salts. Nickel leaves the anodes and deposits itself on the cathodes. The other metals do not.

Unfortunately the situation is not quite so simple, for when a high enough e.m.f. is used to plate the nickel, other metals such as copper and iron plate too. An unusual twist is given to the system to prevent impurities from plating-out. The cathode is placed inside a canvas box immersed in the electrolyte. Electrolyte surrounding the anode is continuously pumped away to a purification plant where the unwanted metal ions (and sulphur if sulphide anodes are used) are removed from the solution by purely chemical means. The metals are taken out of solution as precipitates and the solids are simply filtered out. The purified electrolyte is pumped into the canvas box surrounding the cathode, but at an increased pressure so that the liquid level in the box is higher than that surrounding it. Liquid is therefore continuously forcing its way out through the pores in the box, so preventing the outer impure liquid from seeping in to reach the cathode. As nickel ions are the only metallic ions present they are the only ones to be plated. The resulting cathode nickel is 99·9% pure.

The Carbonyl Process

This is based on the discovery by Dr. Ludwig Mond that at a temperature of 40–50°C nickel will combine with carbon monoxide gas to form another gas, nickel carbonyl.

$$Ni + 4CO \rightarrow Ni(CO)_4$$

nickel   carbon monoxide   nickel carbonyl

When this gas is more strongly heated, it splits up again into nickel and carbon monoxide gas.

$$Ni(CO)_4 \rightarrow Ni + 4CO$$

nickel carbonyl — nickel — carbon monoxide

Furthermore, nickel is the only metal which will do this at these temperatures and atmospheric pressure.

The starting point is the conversion of the nickel oxide calcine to metallic nickel by completely reducing it with water gas. (A mixture of hydrogen and carbon monoxide.) The hydrogen removes the oxygen to form water, leaving behind the uncombined nickel.

The impure nickel forms nickel carbonyl in towers called *volatilizers*. The powder takes a downward path through the tower while the carbon monoxide blown upwards carries off the nickel as gaseous nickel carbonyl. As heat is given out by this reaction, the vessel is water cooled to ensure that the right temperature is maintained. The impurities are left behind as solids as they cannot become gases.

The carbonyl gas from the volatilizer passes into a *decomposer* and in its hot interior decomposes, depositing its nickel onto small nickel pellets which gradually grow as they circulate through and through the decomposer. The carbon monoxide released is returned to the volatilizer to make more nickel carbonyl gas. Once more, nickel of high purity has been made.

THE COINAGE METALS

Copper

Copper was probably the first metal ever to be extracted from its ores. It still ranks as one of the important metals of the present age. It is in great demand for electrical wiring, overhead cables etc., because within the range of cheaper metals it is by far the best conductor of electricity.

Copper is mainly found in the form of compounds, but, as might be expected of a fairly unreactive metal, it is sometimes found as the element itself. There are over 140 naturally occurring copper compounds but only a few of them are important as ores from which copper is extracted. Most of them occur only in small quantities. Many are compounds of sulphur. This is because the copper and sulphur were originally thrown up together in volcanic regions.

Most copper is extracted from copper pyrites, also known as chalcopyrite. The raw copper extracted from ores is not pure enough for electrical purposes and is further purified by electrolysis. A block of impure copper is immersed in copper sulphate solution and connected to the positive

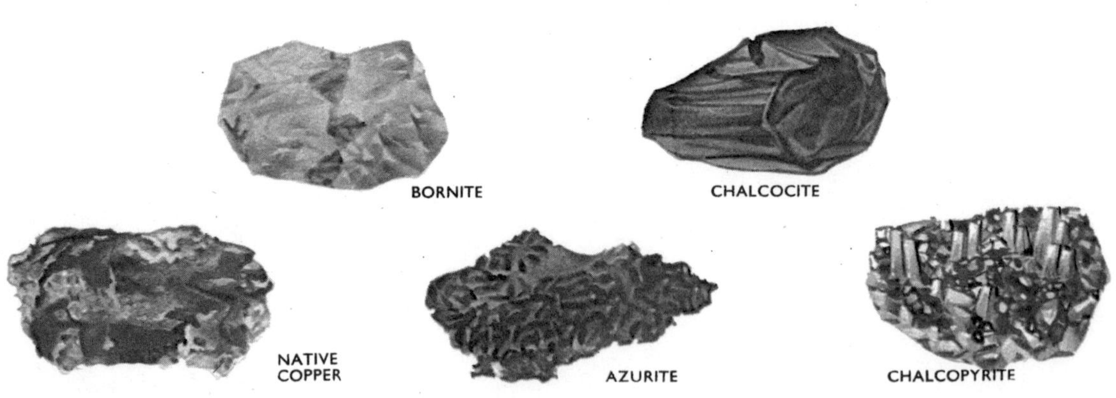

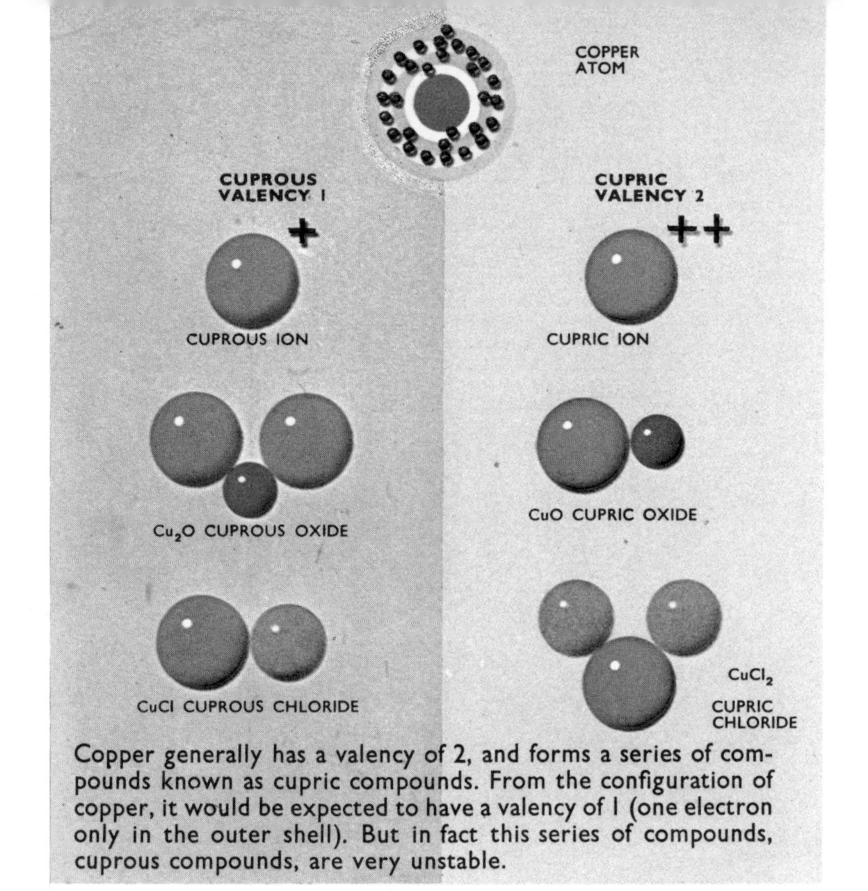

Copper generally has a valency of 2, and forms a series of compounds known as cupric compounds. From the configuration of copper, it would be expected to have a valency of I (one electron only in the outer shell). But in fact this series of compounds, cuprous compounds, are very unstable.

terminal of a direct current electricity supply (i.e. as the anode) and a thin sheet of pure copper is connected to the negative terminal as the cathode. Copper ions drift across the solution from the anode to the cathode and while the anode is eaten away the cathode grows as pure copper is deposited on it. The impurities either go into solution or drop down to the bottom. The gold and silver in the mud which collects underneath the anode are often sufficient to pay for the refining process. Gold and silver are closely related to copper and tiny quantities are often found with it.

Copper is made into a great many alloys of which bronze (copper and tin) is probably the best known; it is much harder wearing than pure copper. All hard-wearing copper alloys are now known as bronzes. The coming of bronze changed the entire way of life of Stone Age man. The new, sharp bronze weapons made the killing of animals for food much easier and made organised warfare possible.

Copper has three complete shells of electrons and only one electron in its outer shell. From this it would be expected to have a valency of one, and in fact copper does have a valency of one in a series of compounds known as *cuprous* compounds. Each cuprous ion has lost its outer electron, making the ion positively charged. Strangely enough cuprous ions are very unstable, for although copper should have a valency of one, it prefers to have a valency of two. An electron from an inner shell is lost as well as the outer one making a *cupric* (valency 2) ion. *Cuprous* compounds are very unstable and easily become *cupric* compounds which are much more stable.

Copper compounds give a greenish-blue coloration to the flame of a Bunsen burner and most of the salts are blue in colour. They are also poisonous. For this reason copper sulphate solution is used for killing unwanted fungi growing on vines.

Cupric ions have a tendency to gather round them four molecules of water, both in solution and when in a solid, crystalline form. This water is loosely bound and if crystals of copper sulphate, for example, are heated the water is driven off and the crystal structure collapses. Ammonia also tends to group itself round cupric ions. Cupric salts will dissolve in ammonia solution to form a complex cuprammonium compound in which four molecules of ammonia are grouped around each cupric ion. This cuprammonium complex is capable of dissolving cellulose and has been tried as a means of making rayon.

The Cyanide Process is used for the extraction of both gold and silver. (Below) *Large tanks in which the cyanide solution reacts with silver ores.* (Left) *Flow diagram for the whole process.*

Silver and Gold

Silver and gold are, perhaps, the two most important of the *noble* metals, so called because they do not tarnish in air or water and are only attacked by strong acids. On account of this they were long used for coinage. Both of these metals have been known for several thousand years, and objects made from them have been found during excavations at the centres of early civilizations, particularly in Egypt.

In contrast with many metals which only occur in Nature as chemical compounds, both silver and gold are found as the elements themselves. It is for this reason that these metals were known to the ancients. Although silver and gold may be found in a fairly pure state, it is more frequent for the deposits to contain alloys of silver, gold and copper. The occurrence of copper, silver and gold together is not really surprising since they are chemically related and are all in the same chemical family in the Periodic Table.

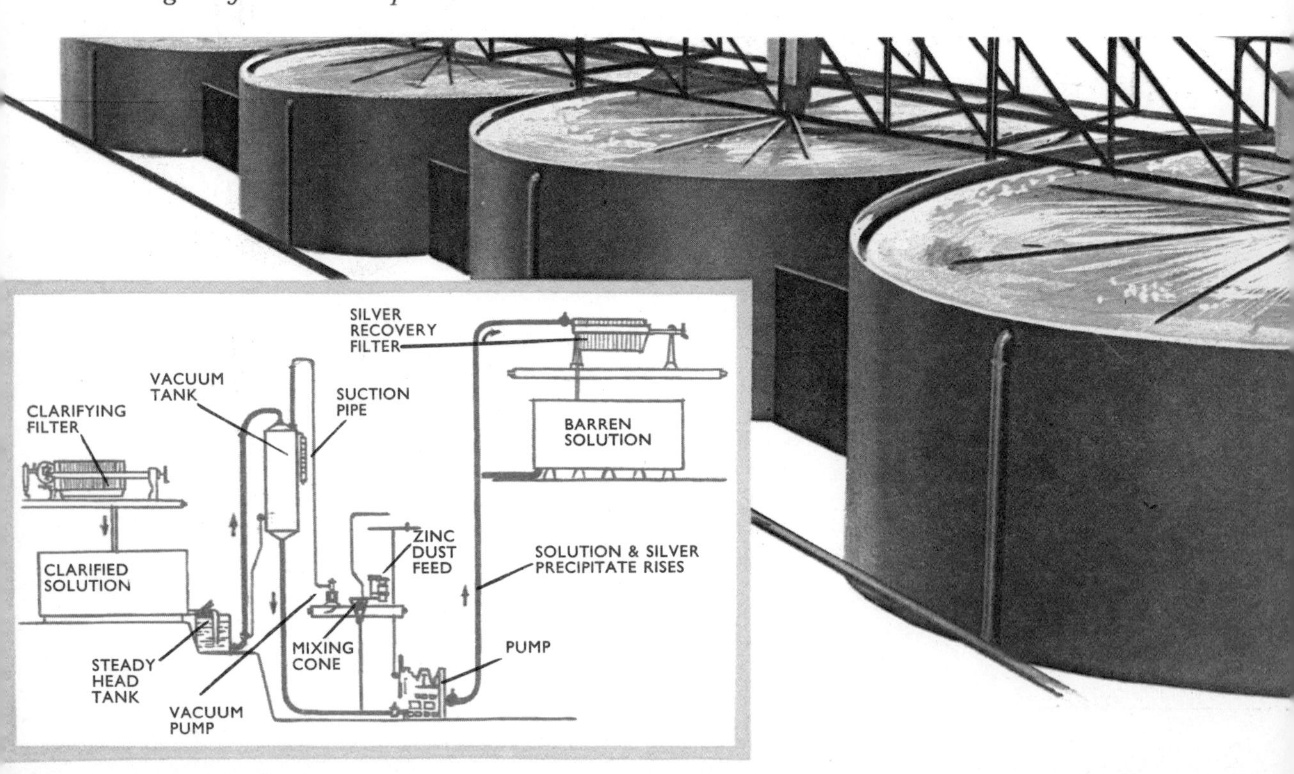

In the Parkes Process for desilvering lead, zinc (in which silver is much more soluble) is added to the molten lead-silver alloy. After thorough mixing, the zinc-silver layer floats to the top and is skimmed off. (Right) *A thin protective layer of silver has been deposited by electrolysis on this large 'basket' for a centrifuge.*

Silver

Silver is obtained principally as a by-product when lead, zinc and copper ores are refined. However, it is also obtained from ores mined for their silver content, the commonest of which is *argentite*, a sulphide of silver. This and other silver ores are widely distributed over the American continent, but nowhere is silver to be found in large quantities. The principal world source is in Mexico which produces 35% of the world output (about 6,000 tons per year).

Of the many processes which have been developed over the years, the *cyanide process* is normally used now in extracting silver from argentite. After the ore has been crushed, it is ground to a fine powder in a ball mill which also contains weak sodium cyanide solution. The silver sulphide and also any free silver present react with the sodium cyanide to yield sodium argentocyanide, $Na[Ag(CN)_2]$, which is soluble in water.

The suspension is agitated with compressed air for several days. This serves to oxidize the sodium sulphide formed by the reaction between silver sulphide and sodium cyanide. The solution of sodium argentocyanide is then filtered and the dissolved air removed by vacuum. The silver is finally displaced from solution by adding a suspension of finely powdered zinc dust.

The precipitated silver is filtered off and dried. This product contains at least 75% silver, but will always contain impurities, particularly the excess of zinc dust. Further purification is, therefore, necessary.

As about 75% of the world output of lead is obtained from ores which also contain silver, it follows that the recovery of silver is a profitable stage in refining lead. One way of doing this is by the *Parkes Process*. After removing other impurities, namely copper, antimony, arsenic and tin, from the molten lead-silver alloy, zinc is added to the bath. Silver is much more soluble in zinc than in lead, so that after mixing the contents of the bath most of the silver migrates to the layer of molten zinc which floats on top of the lead. When the temperature of the bath is allowed to fall, the zinc-silver alloy is skimmed off as it solidifies on the surface. The zinc can then be distilled off leaving behind the silver which has a higher melting point.

Silver is a white metal which has good resistance to the action of most substances. It is unaffected by pure air or oxygen but is easily tarnished when there are traces of hydrogen sulphide in the air. A layer of black silver sulphide is formed on the metallic surface. The film which appears on silver egg spoons is caused by the action between organic sulphur compounds and the silver. Silver is attacked by the halogens (chlorine, bromine and iodine). It is unaffected by alkalis and only reacts with a few acids – hot concentrated sulphuric acid and dilute nitric acid.

Silver is the best conductor of heat and electricity but copper is often used in its place because it is cheaper. However, silver is sometimes used in chemical plants. Its good resistance to corrosion and comparatively high melting point (960°C) commend it, in addition to its high conductivity.

Thus reaction vessels and reboilers in distillation columns are sometimes lined with silver. The tubes of heat exchangers may also be made of silver. Silver is also used in various types of electrical apparatus. It is particularly valuable in contact breakers, as in control units for traffic lights. A number of alloys of silver are of industrial importance. Silver-copper-zinc and silver-phosphorus-copper alloys are used in joining metal by *brazing*. But by far the greatest quantity of silver is used in making photographic materials.

Gold

Native gold occurs in quartz veins from which some of the fine particles have been washed out by rain water. Hence gold is also found mixed with sand in the beds of streams. There are deposits in Central and North America, in Australia, South Africa and Eastern Europe.

The gold particles are separated from the alluvial sand or gravel or crushed quartz by washing in shallow troughs which are vibrated. The gold, which is much more dense than the sand, settles out and is retained in the bottom of the troughs, by battens. Before this sedimentation process was organized on a large scale, it used to be carried out in small pans in an operation known as *panning*.

Gold may also be recovered from

A large mill in which gold-bearing rock is ground to a powder before it is treated with cyanide solution.

crushed quartz or from the residues left after the extraction of other metals by the *cyanide process.* This works in much the same way as for the extraction of silver from its ores. Gold reacts with potassium cyanide solution and soluble potassium auro-cyanide $K[Au(CN)_2]$ is obtained. After aeration, the gold is precipitated by adding zinc.

Gold is a bright yellow metal of high density (19·3 gm./cc.). It is a good conductor of heat and electricity and resists the action of almost all single acids. It does, however, react with a mixture of concentrated nitric acid and concentrated hydrochloric acid. Because this mixture of acids (in the ratio 1 : 4) is able to dissolve gold it is called *aqua regia.* Gold does not tarnish in air. The pure metal is rather soft – even for jewellery – and is generally used in alloys with other metals – silver, palladium and platinum – to give it added strength without loss of corrosion resistance.

In addition to its uses in jewellery and for ornaments, gold has a number of important uses in industry where a non-tarnishable surface is required. Gold (in sheet or electro-deposit form) is used for lining selected vessels in chemical plants.

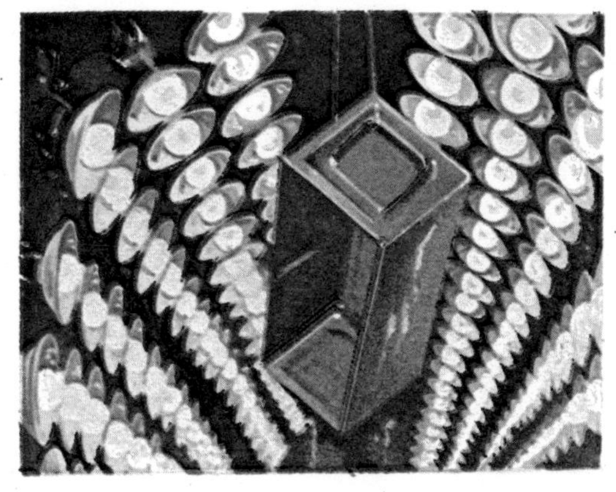

As gold takes and retains a high polish (i.e. *does not tarnish*) *it is valuable as a reflecting surface. Here gold-plated reflectors are used in an infra-red heating unit. These are much used in industry for baking and drying paints, enamels and varnishes. The object is passed slowly down the infra-red oven and rapid drying is obtained.*

Zinc, Cadmium and Mercury

Zinc

Zinc always occurs in nature as a compound, the most common being zinc blende, the sulphide of zinc (ZnS), and calamine, zinc carbonate ($ZnCO_3$).

When the ores are mined they are by no means pure and contain considerable amounts of useless material which must be removed. The ore is concentrated by crushing the lumps to a powder and pouring the powder into a stream of water. The unwanted material sinks to the bottom and the concentrated ore is skimmed off the top. Before the metal can be extracted by smelting, the ores have to be converted into oxides. To do this, the concentrated ores are 'roasted' or heated strongly in a current of air. The carbon in carbonate ores is blown away as carbon dioxide and the sulphur in sulphide ores becomes the gas, sulphur dioxide.

$ZnCO_3$	$\rightarrow ZnO$	$+ CO_2$
zinc carbonate (calamine)	zinc oxide	carbon dioxide

$2ZnS$	$+ 3O_2$	$\rightarrow 2ZnO$	$+ 2SO_2$
zinc sulphide (zinc blende)	oxygen	zinc oxide	sulphur dioxide

Sulphur dioxide is a valuable source of sulphuric acid. Consequently, many zinc plants also run a plant for converting it into the acid. After roasting, the oxide is *smelted*. The oxygen is removed, reducing the oxide to the metal. Anthracite, a comparatively pure form of carbon, acts as the reducing agent to take away the oxygen.

ZnO	$+ C$	$\rightarrow Zn$	$+ CO$
zinc oxide	carbon	zinc	carbon monoxide

The smelting furnace is fed with briquettes made from powdered oxide and powdered anthracite. Although the oxide is mainly that of zinc, it also contains some cadmium oxide. When the furnace is lit, the cadmium impurity comes off first followed by zinc. The metal is driven off as a vapour which passes into a vessel of molten lead. Rotors dipping into the molten lead whisk small droplets of it up into the path of the vapour. The zinc in the vapour dissolves in the droplets. In this way the furnace gases are swept free from their load of metal vapour. The lead solution is allowed to cool slightly. Lead is a heavy metal. Zinc is much lighter and floats on top of it. The floating zinc overflows and solidifies in a neighbouring bath. The lead is used over and over again. Any remaining cadmium is separated from the zinc by distillation.

Zinc in the powdered form very readily burns in air giving off clouds of the finely powdered white oxide.

$2Zn$	$+ \ O_2$	$\rightarrow 2ZnO$
zinc	oxygen	zinc oxide

Hot zinc reacts with steam and becomes an oxide.

Zn	$+ \ H_2O$	$\rightarrow ZnO$	$+ H_2$
zinc	water	zinc oxide	hydrogen

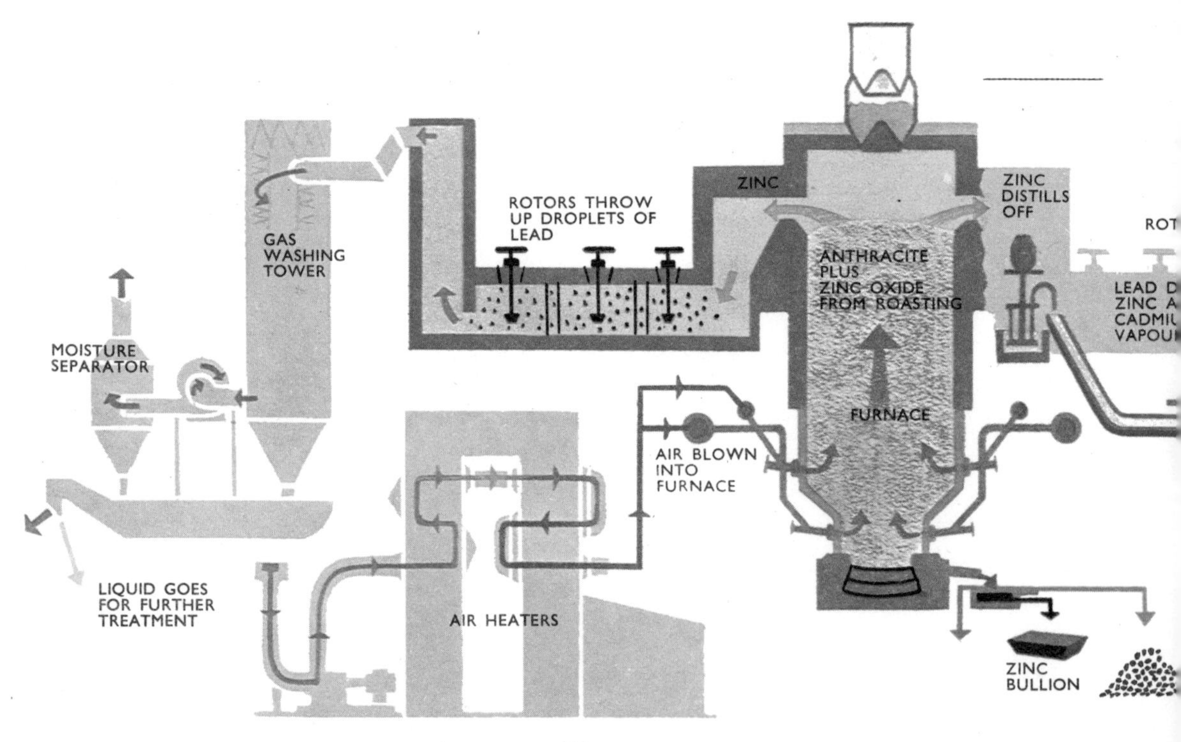

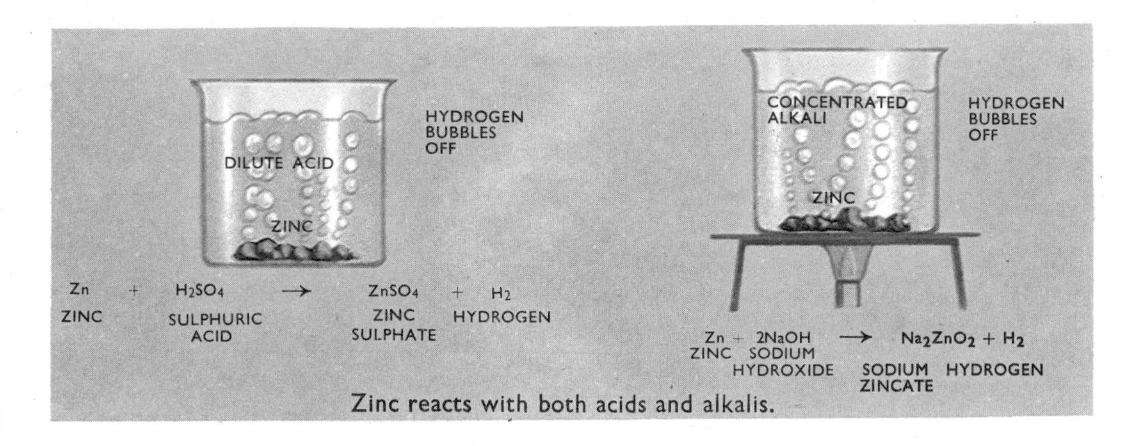

Zinc reacts with both acids and alkalis.

It dissolves in acids to form salts. Hydrogen is given off by the reaction. But unlike most metals, zinc will also dissolve in hot concentrated alkalis.

Zn	+	$2NaOH$	$\rightarrow$	Na_2ZnO_2	+	H_2
zinc		sodium hydroxide		sodium zincate		hydrogen

Zinc oxide, a white powder which is yellow when it is hot, will react with acids. This is normal behaviour, for oxides of metals (basic oxides) all do this. But it will also behave like the oxide of a non-metal (acidic oxide) and react with alkalis. Because it has both acidic and basic properties it is known as an *amphoteric* oxide. Zinc hydroxide is also amphoteric, reacting with both acids and alkalis.

Many of the compounds of zinc are similar to those of cadmium in their behaviour. For example, when hydrogen sulphide is bubbled through solutions of the salts of zinc (alkaline solution) or cadmium, solid sulphides are precipitated. Zinc sulphide comes down as a thick white powder and cadmium sulphide as a deep yellow one.

GAS TO WASHING PLANT

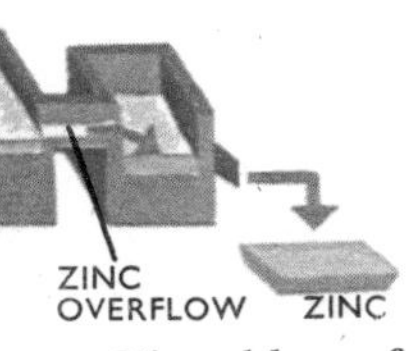

Zinc blast furnace in which zinc oxide is smelted with anthracite. The zinc comes off as a vapour and dissolves in the droplets of lead thrown up by the rotors.

Use of zinc

A great deal of zinc is used for coating iron to prevent it from rusting. This galvanised iron has a mottled appearance because of the formation of large zinc crystals. Zinc is also used to prevent the hulls of ships from rusting. This is not done by coating the hull but by placing slabs of zinc at intervals over the surface. This is known as *cathodic protection.* The iron of the hull does not have exactly the same composition throughout and because of this small electrical currents flow from the iron to the sea water and back to a different piece of iron. Rusting occurs where the currents leave the iron. When pieces of zinc are stuck on the surface, the currents leave from them and they corrode away instead. Zinc is also mixed with other metals and the alloy cast into various metal parts such as the frameworks of loudspeakers and the numbers of car number-plates. Brass is a better known alloy of copper and zinc. Flashlight batteries have zinc cases. Zinc oxide is commercially the most important zinc compound. The pigment Chinese white is made from it. It has the advantage over lead oxide that it does not blacken in hydrogen sulphide laden air.

Cadmium

Cadmium has only one well-known

Zinc and cadmium owe their similarities to their similar atomic structures.

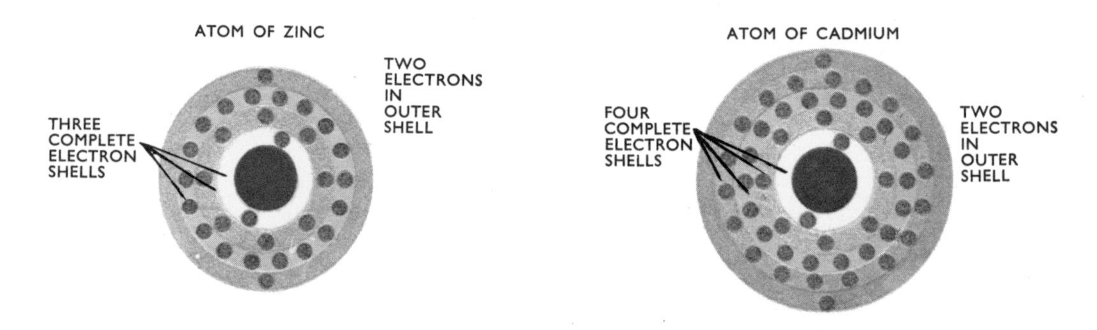

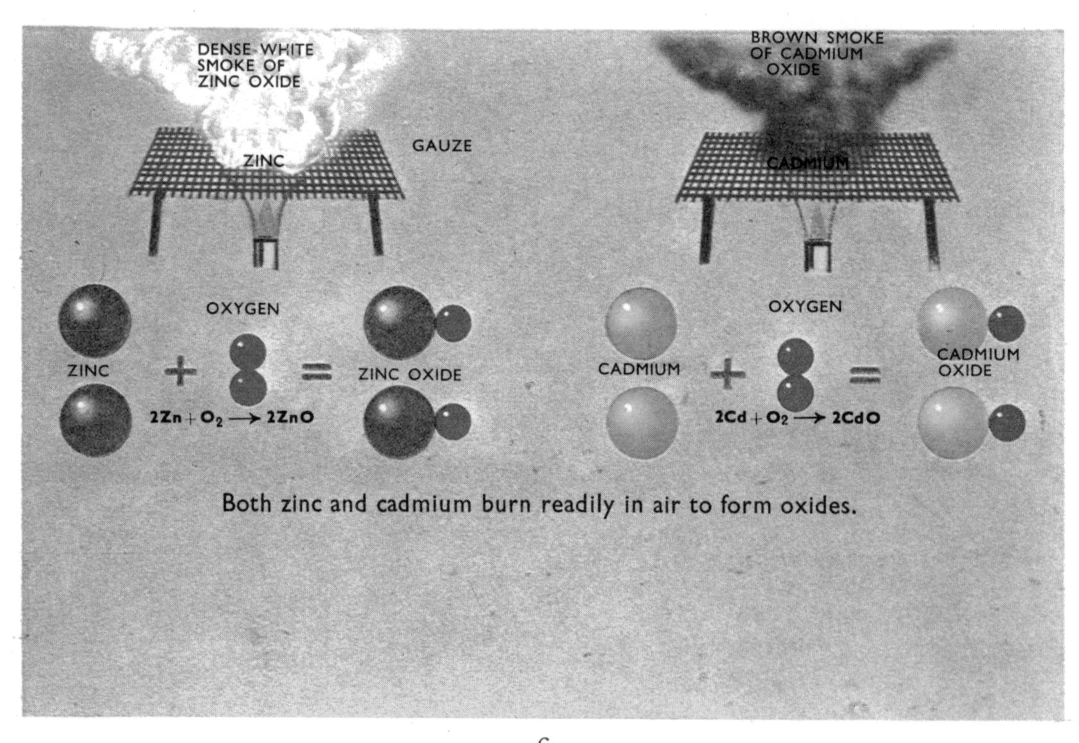

Both zinc and cadmium burn readily in air to form oxides.

mineral, greenockite, cadmium sulphide (CdS), and even that is extremely rare. Most cadmium compounds are found intermingled with the ores of zinc. It is not worth while to mine greenockite to produce cadmium as the metal is satisfactorily extracted as a by-product when zinc is manufactured from its ores.

Powdered cadmium burns in air to give clouds of brown oxide. Hot cadmium will also react with steam to form an oxide. It will dissolve in acids to form salts, giving off hydrogen, but it will not dissolve in hot concentrated alkalis (compare with zinc). When hydrogen sulphide is bubbled through a solution of a cadmium salt, deep yellow solid cadmium sulphide is precipitated.

Cadmium is becoming increasingly important for plating electrical parts. Cadmium sulphide, the yellow pigment, is used in paints. Overhead electrical cables are made from copper alloyed with 10% of cadmium.

Mercury

Mercury is one of the oldest metals known to man. A small flask of it was found in a Mesopotamian grave dating from about the 16th century B.C. It was certainly known to the ancient Romans, who obtained it from the mine at Monte Amiata. Pliny described the metal as quicksilver (a 'live' metal), a name by which it is called today.

Monte Amiata is still the most important mine in Italy, second only in importance to the ancient mine at Almaden in Spain. Apart from in Spain and Italy, it occurs in association with the volcanic areas of the world, such as in Central America, Japan, Russia and China.

As mercury is so easy to extract from its ores, the methods of extracting it have undergone very little change. It is mined as the deep red mineral, *cinnabar*, whose chemical name is mercuric sulphide (HgS). When cinnabar is heated strongly it decomposes (the roasting furnaces are usually gas or oil fired). Mercury distils off as a vapour, and when the vapour is cooled in a condenser the mercury liquefies. This can be performed quite easily in a laboratory. The simplicity of the method is demonstrated by the fact that in Mexico today many prospectors distil their own mercury. They have small distillation pots which they carry around strapped to their backs. These can be filled with ore, a fire lit underneath and the vapour passed through a water-cooled coil to condense it. Finance houses buy the mercury from the prospectors in a similar way to that used by the gold-rush finance houses.

Cinnabar. *The mineral ore from which mercury is extracted.*

Unwanted solid material can be removed from mercury by filtering it through a chamois leather. This is also very useful for cleaning dirty mercury in the laboratory. Where the very pure metal is required, it is usual after filtration to redistil it in a vacuum, and then wash it with dilute nitric acid by dripping the mercury down a tower so that it cascades through a column of the acid. It can be finally purified by electrolysis.

Mercury has the ability to 'dissolve' most metals, forming *amalgams* with them. (An amalgam is a solution of metal in mercury.) Fortunately, because iron does not dissolve in mercury it can be stored in steel flasks, each usually containing 76 pounds of mercury. (Mercury has been sold in 76-pound flasks since Roman times.) The annual world production is at present about 230,000 flasks, with Spain and Italy as the principal producers.

Mercury is the only metal to be a liquid at room temperature. It is an exceptional liquid for it does not wet the sides of the vessel containing it. A finger dipped in it is quite dry on removal. It is very dense, weighing 13·6 times as much as an equal volume of water. If mercury is poured into an ordinary glass test tube, the force of its fall usually smashes the bottom of the tube. Hard glass test tubes must be used.

It is not surprising that mercury is so dense, for it has the high atomic weight of 200·6. The atoms are built up with two electrons in the outermost unfilled electron shell. From this, mercury would be expected to have a valency of *two*, and indeed this is its valency when it forms its most stable series of compounds, the *mercuric* compounds. Examples are mercuric oxide (HgO) and mercuric chloride ($HgCl_2$). It also forms a series of less stable compounds; the *mercurous* compounds where the mercury has a valency of only *one*. Examples are mercurous chloride (Hg_2Cl_2) and mercurous sulphate (Hg_2SO_4). Mercury combines with chlorine and bromine at room temperatures, and dissolves readily in nitric acid, but it is largely unaffected by dilute hydrochloric or sulphuric acids, or by alkalis.

When mercury is heated in air, red flakes of mercuric oxide form on its surface. Stronger heating decomposes them, forming mercury and oxygen. Lavoisier used this fact to find the proportion of oxygen in the air. The heated mercury removed the oxygen but not the nitrogen.

Mercury vapour and most mercury compounds are very poisonous and consequently must be handled with very great care. Because of this, rigid rules are laid down in factories using them. Although mercury vapour can

The ores of mercury are crushed and then heated, to vaporise the metal. From the rotary furnaces the vapour passes through ducts into condensers.

be absorbed through the skin, poisoning usually occurs by breathing in the vapour. The first sign is the appearance of a blue line on bleeding swollen gums. Later on the victim begins to totter drunkenly and may even start 'seeing things'. The poor Mad Hatter was not really mad. He was suffering from mercury poisoning, a common occurrence among hatters who use mercuric nitrate when making felt hats from rabbit fur.

The largest use of mercury is in the manufacture of caustic soda and chlorine. Here, the mercury forms the cathode in the electrolysis of brine. Sodium dissolves as an amalgam in the cathode and is later converted into caustic soda. During the electrolysis, chlorine is evolved.

The second largest use is in electrical appliances. Mercury vapour lamps and fluorescent tubes are filled with vapour. When the vapour is ionised, it conducts electricity and excited ions and molecules emit light. The colour of the light varies with the vapour pressure of the mercury. Mercury forms the cathode in the mercury arc rectifier which changes alternating current into one-way direct current. The rectifier consists of an evacuated glass envelope with an iron anode and mercury cathode. Some of the mercury is vaporised in the valve when an arc is struck between a 'starting' anode and the cathode. This vapour, when ionised, is capable of carrying very large currents, but only in one direction, so producing rectification. Many electrical switches also use mercury to make and break electrical contact. This is because, being a fluid, the mercury can completely surround a contact, thus creating excellent electrical continuity, as well as overcoming the problem of 'pitting' which arises in solid contact points in switches.

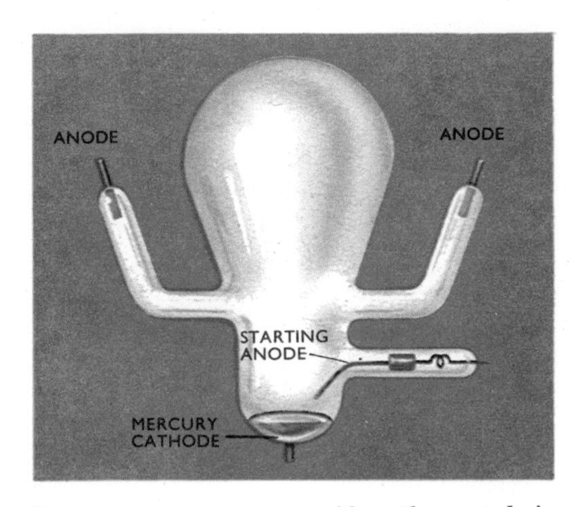

In the mercury arc rectifier the metal is vaporized by means of the starting anode, and the main current is carried in the ionized vapour.

Mercury is of course used in instruments such as thermometers and barometers.

One of the major faults of dry batteries is that bubbles of hydrogen collect on the cathodic surfaces, preventing them from working properly. The addition of mercury salts prevents this from happening and has led to the manufacture of very stable midget batteries which are used in satellites and electric wrist-watches.

Mercury salts are useful poisons because they can be very effective in controlling bacterial and fungal infections occurring in many of the most important industrial processes. In agriculture, *calomel* (mercurous chloride) is used for control of moss in lawns, and phenyl mercury compounds are used to protect many crop seeds (especially cereals) from fungal diseases during germination. Other organic mercury salts are used for fruit sprays, cotton plant treatment,

Mercury is normally stored in steel flasks, each of which contains 76 *pounds of the liquid.*

sugar cane dip, protection of rubber trees and many other applications. These compounds are also added to paint to prevent bacteria spoiling the paint in the can and to control mildew on the paint film after application. When paint looks dirty this is often due to a growth of mildew. Mercuric oxide paint is used on ships' hulls to control the growth of barnacles, for when ships become encrusted their speed is cut considerably. The water systems of pulp and paper mills are frequently treated with mercury compounds to kill off bacteria which would otherwise make them slimy and foul, and to preserve the pulp from discolorations produced by fungi during storage prior to use in paper manufacture. Mercury salts are very efficient preservatives for a wide range of products including hides and skins, glues, some cosmetics and blood plasma.

A number of compounds of mercury have medicinal uses and others are employed as catalysts in chemical processes. Mercuric thiocyanate made into small pills with gum tragacanth is used for indoor fireworks. On ignition these give a snake-like voluminous ash known as Pharaoh's Serpent. Ground with chalk, mercury gives a fine grey powder used in fingerprint detection. Mercuric sulphide is the red pigment *vermilion.*

The Families at the Centre

CHAPTER SEVEN

Group 4

Carbon and its Inorganic Compounds

For centuries the diamond has been much sought after as a gem-stone. Its great attraction, compared with most gems, is its brilliance due to the multitude of reflections of light falling upon the cut stone. Diamonds were originally thought to be rare, but a number of important finds in the Republic of South Africa have necessitated a strict control on the export of new diamonds in order to maintain their market value.

Diamond is but one form of the element carbon; another is the black, greasy powder known as graphite. Although both contain identical carbon atoms, the structures of these two forms (*allotropes*) have marked differences. The great strength of diamond can be explained in part by the regular arrangement of its atoms in space. Each atom is linked to its four nearest neighbours—four bonds are equally arranged in space around each atom. In contrast, the atoms of graphite exist in layers which are only loosely held together. Three of the bonds link the atom to three other atoms in the layer, while the fourth holds that layer to the next layer either above or below. The latter bond is longer and weaker than the other three, and permits adjacent layers of carbon atoms to slide easily over one another.

Only those diamonds which are clear and have a natural sparkle are used in jewellery. Other diamonds which are inferior in appearance have valuable uses industrially. Diamond is the hardest substance known, and as such is valuable in tipping cutting tools, from the small diamond points which are used for cutting or engraving glass to the large drills for various mining operations. Graphite is used as a lubricant, and in the manufacture of 'lead' pencils and rods for carbon arc lamps. Some electric furnaces are lined with graphite bricks and very pure graphite is used in large quantities in the construction of nuclear reactors.

Carbon is present in all organic compounds and is an essential constituent of all plant and animal cells.

Artificial Diamonds

Both diamonds and graphite are allotropic forms of the same element. Because of the great value of diamonds and the relative cheapness of graphite, many people have tried to make diamonds from graphite. Most early attempts were unsuccessful owing to the difficulty of creating the very high pressures and high temperatures needed. The most successful of the pioneers in this field was the French chemist Henri Moissan (1852–1907) who added charcoal to molten iron and quickly cooled the melt. Small diamonds were recovered when the iron was removed by reaction with acid.

Small diamonds for industrial use are now produced commercially from graphite, but the expense of creating the very high pressures makes the diamonds no less expensive than those obtained naturally.

Almost all the substances which burn—certainly those which are generally used as fuels (logs, peat, coal and oil)—contain carbon. This is because many of them are or were once part of living organisms. Peat and coal have been formed during very long periods of time from vegetable matter which has decomposed under pressure in the absence of air. Carbon in the form of charcoal can be obtained from wood by heating logs in such a way that only a small quantity of the wood burns. The heat generated drives off almost all the other substances present to leave behind charcoal which is structurally similar to graphite. Carbon can also be obtained by the carefully controlled heating of other fuels. Thus coal yields coke, which is fairly pure carbon of the graphite type.

Although there is such a large number of compounds containing carbon, the element itself in either of its allotropic forms is comparatively unreactive. If heated strongly in air or oxygen both diamond and graphite burn to yield carbon dioxide. Charcoal also takes fire (but at a lower temperature).

$$\underset{\text{CARBON}}{C} + \underset{\text{OXYGEN}}{O_2} \rightarrow \underset{\text{CARBON DIOXIDE}}{CO_2}$$

If there is a limited supply of oxygen, some of the carbon dioxide may be *reduced* by another reaction with carbon in which carbon monoxide is formed.

$$\underset{\text{CARBON}}{C} + \underset{\text{CARBON DIOXIDE}}{CO_2} \rightarrow \underset{\text{CARBON MONOXIDE}}{2CO}$$

Neither diamond nor graphite is attacked by dilute acids or alkalis. They are slowly oxidized to carbon dioxide by the action of such powerful oxidizing agents as potassium di-

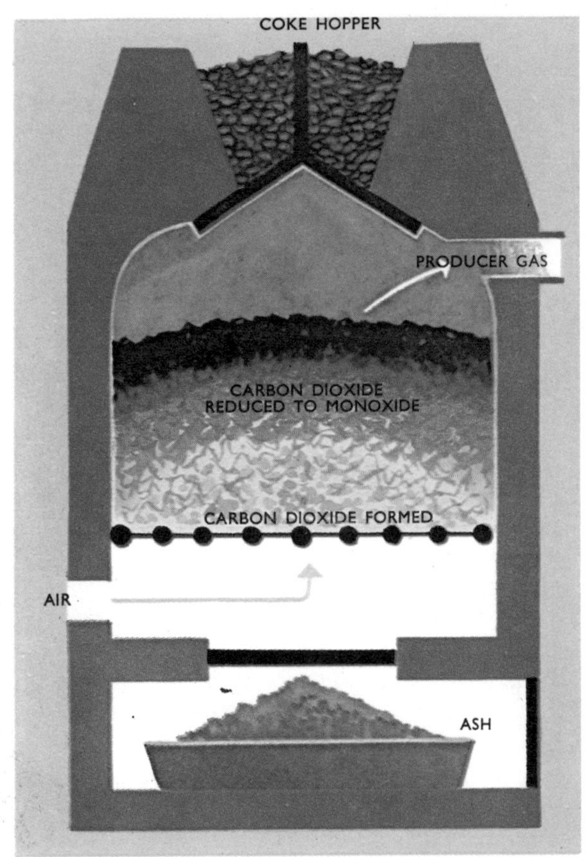

Producer gas, a mixture of carbon monoxide and nitrogen, is formed in a vessel such as this by blowing air through a bed of red-hot coke.

Carbon dioxide is set free if dilute hydrochloric acid is poured on to marble (calcium carbonate) or other metallic carbonates.

chromate acidified with sulphuric acid. Carbon monoxide is formed when either diamond or graphite reacts with molten sodium carbonate.

Carbon monoxide and carbon dioxide are the principal oxides of carbon. They are both colourless gases and both are poisonous, but for different reasons. When air is breathed into the lungs some of the oxygen combines with the haemoglobin of the blood to yield oxyhaemoglobin which is easily decomposed. It is by means of this compound that oxygen is conveyed by the blood around the body. However, if quite a small quantity of carbon monoxide is inhaled it combines with the haemoglobin and a very stable bright red compound—carboxyhaemoglobin—is formed. As a consequence not so much oxyhaemoglobin can be formed and the body becomes starved of oxygen.

Carbon dioxide dissolves in the blood stream and the presence of a

Carbon dioxide, together with sodium silicate, is used in a new method of making sand moulds. The picture shows the wooden pattern of the required metallic casting in position before the sand is added.

large excess of this gas in the air results in an increase in the acidity of the blood. This can in turn upset the balance of the respiratory system. Although large excesses of carbon dioxide in the blood can be fatal, a certain minimum concentration is necessary to stimulate breathing. A reduction in the proportion of oxygen in the air is far less dangerous than an increase in the proportion of carbon dioxide.

Carbon monoxide burns with a blue flame. As a reasonable quantity of heat is released when the gas burns, and as it can be produced quite easily and cheaply, it is used industrially as a fuel. In practice a mixture of carbon monoxide and nitrogen, known as *producer gas*, is made by blowing air through a bed of red-hot coke in a closed vessel called a gas-producer. This gas is used extensively in industry, but it does not give out so much heat as the same volume of household gas.

Carbon dioxide is a colourless, dense gas which dissolves in water. A solution of the gas in water contains a small quantity of carbonic acid, the salts of which are known as carbonates. Carbon dioxide does not burn and very few substances will continue to burn when placed in the gas. Magnesium, sodium and potassium are exceptions. Magnesium *reduces* the carbon dioxide to carbon and is itself oxidized to magnesium oxide:

$$\underset{\text{MAGNESIUM}}{2Mg} + \underset{\text{CARBON DIOXIDE}}{CO_2} \rightarrow \underset{\text{MAGNESIUM OXIDE}}{2MgO} + \underset{\text{CARBON}}{C}$$

As carbon dioxide is dense and also cheap it is much used in fire extinguishers for ordinary fires, though it should not be used on magnesium fires.

Carbon dioxide is obtained as a by-product in the fermentation of sugars in the manufacture of beer and spirits, and this is the principal commercial source. The gas is given out during the process of breathing, but a balance in the composition of the atmosphere is maintained because green plants take in carbon dioxide. They use it in the process of *photosynthesis*.

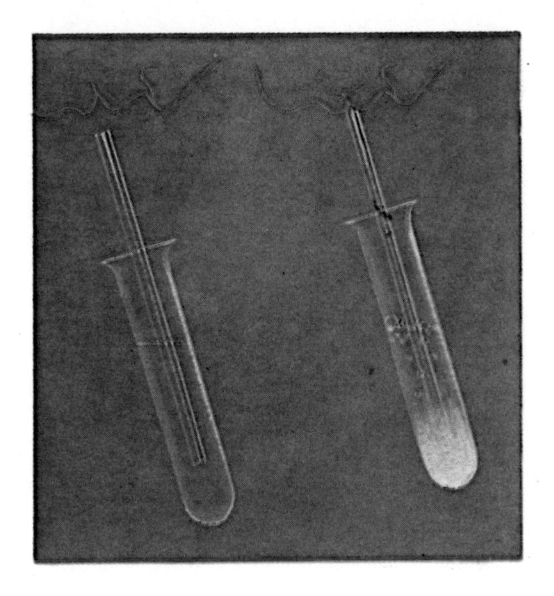

If carbon dioxide gas is bubbled through a clear solution of calcium hydroxide, the liquid becomes cloudy due to the formation of white grains of calcium carbonate. Exhaled air contains carbon dioxide.

The presence of carbon dioxide in air which is breathed out of the lungs can be shown by blowing into a test tube containing lime water (a very dilute solution of calcium hydroxide). Small particles of insoluble calcium carbonate are formed. These are white and give the solution a cloudy appearance. This is used as a test for carbon dioxide.

Silica, the dioxide of silicon, is familiar in various guises, which include quartz, flint, granite, amethyst, rock-crystal and sand. Silicon is in fact the second most abundant element in the Ear h's crust (the most abundant is oxygen). It can be obtained from its oxide by heating with powdered magnesium, a reducing agent, in a covered crucible.

Separation is carried out by hydrochloric acid which converts the insoluble magnesium oxide into a soluble salt, magnesium chloride, so that the silicon can be filtered out.

For many years the element silicon was of no commercial importance, but recent developments have shown that in a high state of purity it is a valuable alternative to germanium in the construction of transistors and other semi-conductor devices. Silicon transistors are particularly useful for operating at high temperatures.

Silicon is a dark-grey, opaque solid which has a crystal structure rather similar to that of diamond – each silicon atom is attached to its four nearest neighbours. Silicon is quite inert at low temperatures, but when strongly heated in air the surface becomes covered with a layer of oxide. Silicon is insoluble in water and resists the action of most acids, but not hydrofluoric. When boiled with alkaline hydroxides, such as caustic soda, sodium silicate is formed:

$$\underset{\text{Silicon}}{Si} + \underset{\text{Sodium Hydroxide}}{2NaOH} + \underset{\text{Water}}{H_2O} \rightarrow \underset{\text{Sodium Silicate}}{Na_2SiO_3} + \underset{\text{Hydrogen}}{2H_2}$$

Silicon combines with fluorine and chlorine when heated in either of these gases and the corresponding silicon halide is formed.

Silicon itself is not very hard, but silicon carbide (known commercially as carborundum), which is obtained by heating a mixture of silicon dioxide (silica) and coke in an electric furnace, is almost as hard as diamond. Crystals of carborundum are hard, chemically inactive, and do not decompose until heated to about 2,200°C. Crushed crystals of this compound can be mixed with a binder such as clay and moulded into various shapes for use as grindstones and grinding wheels. The blocks and wheels have to be baked subsequently, so that the individual crystals fuse together.

As silicon is situated immediately below carbon in the same family in the periodic table, one might expect the compounds of the elements to be similar. This is true to some considerable extent, but there is very little in common physically between the oxides of carbon and silicon. Carbon dioxide is a gas at normal temperatures, whereas silicon dioxide is a hard solid which melts at 1,730°C.

The stability of the silica (silicon dioxide) in its crystalline state is attributed to the structure of the molecules. Carbon dioxide, even in the solid state, comprises CO_2 units in which two oxygen atoms are joined by double bonds to each carbon. In contrast, the silicon molecules in silicon dioxide are joined by single bonds to four oxygen atoms.

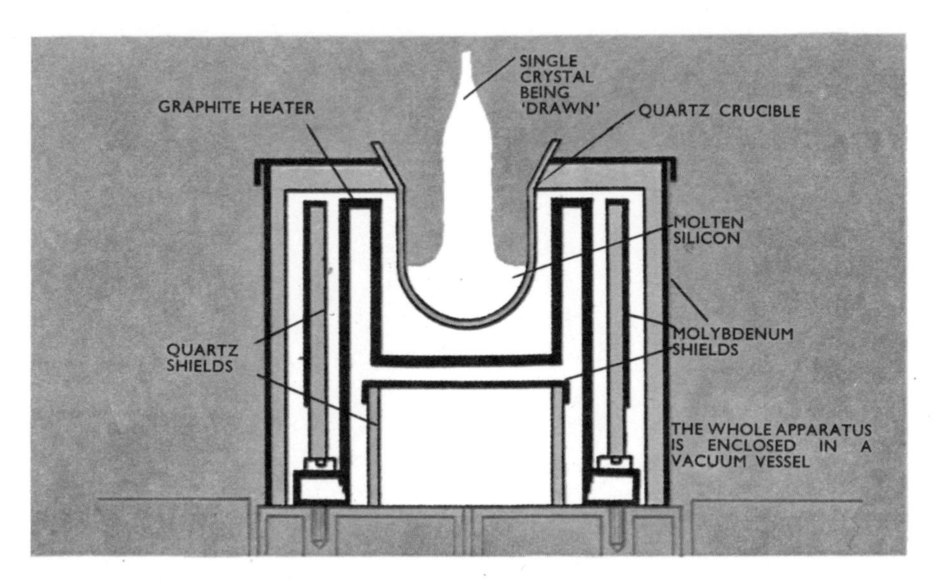

Diagram of the heater unit in which refined silicon is melted. Single crystals of silicon for use in transistors are then drawn from the melt.

The other bond of each oxygen atom is linked to a different silicon atom. Thus each oxygen atom is shared between two silicon atoms. The existence of this *macromolecule*, as such a giant network of silicon and oxygen atoms is known, accounts for the extraordinary stability of silica (e.g. sand).

In addition to the use of sand and various silica-containing stones in the building trade, silica has many other uses, particularly the manufacture of glass from silica, sodium carbonate and lime.

A rather special type of glass can be obtained by heating quartz until it melts, and then working the molten mass in much the same way as glass. Quartz glass fibres are used for suspensions in delicate electrical apparatus. Crucibles, evaporating dishes, and similar apparatus made from fused silica are useful for certain types of reactions. At high temperatures silica will combine with bases and metallic oxides to yield silicates, so there is a limit to the reactions for which silica ware is suitable.

In recent years a whole range of silicon-containing organic compounds – the silicones – has been developed. The basic unit of these compounds is a —Si—O—Si— chain of linkages with two organic groups (methyl, ethyl, phenyl, etc.) attached to each silicon atom in the chain. Most of the silicones are very stable compounds and are not wetted by water. Hence they are used for water-proofing or as water repellents. Depending on the structure of the particular molecules, the silicones may be oils, greases or resins. Some are used as lubricants in situations where there are large temperature variations which would render ordinary oils and greases unsuitable.

When Mendeleef published his Periodic Table of the elements in 1871 he left gaps for elements which had not, at that time, been discovered. Amongst the vacant spaces which he left in the table was one in Group IV immediately beneath silicon.

In 1886 Clemens Winkler isolated a new element which he called germanium. It has properties similar to those of silicon, and furthermore its behaviour was found to correspond very closely with that predicted by Mendeleef for the element missing from Group IV.

Until its semi-conducting properties were discovered almost by accident, germanium had been regarded as a scientific curiosity which had no real use. Although it is a rare element, comparatively large quantities are now required for the manufacture of transistors and rectifiers.

Germanium was found originally in a rare silver-bearing mineral *argyrodite* ($GeS_2.4Ag_2S$) which is found in Germany, but coal is also a useful source. The germanium can most conveniently be recovered from the ash left behind after burning coal, or from the flue dust arising from the combustion of producer gas. Such flue dust may contain as much as 3% germanium.

In extracting the germanium from it, the flue ash is first mixed with powdered coal and soda-ash (anhydrous sodium carbonate) and heated in an oil-fired furnace. As a result of this operation, known as *smelting*, a solid mass containing copper, iron and arsenic as well as germanium and gallium is obtained. While the mixture is molten many of the impurities collect in a layer of slag which is less dense than the metals and floats on top of them.

The metallic mass is then crushed and heated and chlorine gas is passed over it. The germanium tetrachloride and arsenic trichloride formed in the process are volatile liquids at room temperature, and pass over into a condenser. The germanium tetrachloride with its lower boiling point (86°C.) is subsequently separated from arsenic trichloride (boiling point

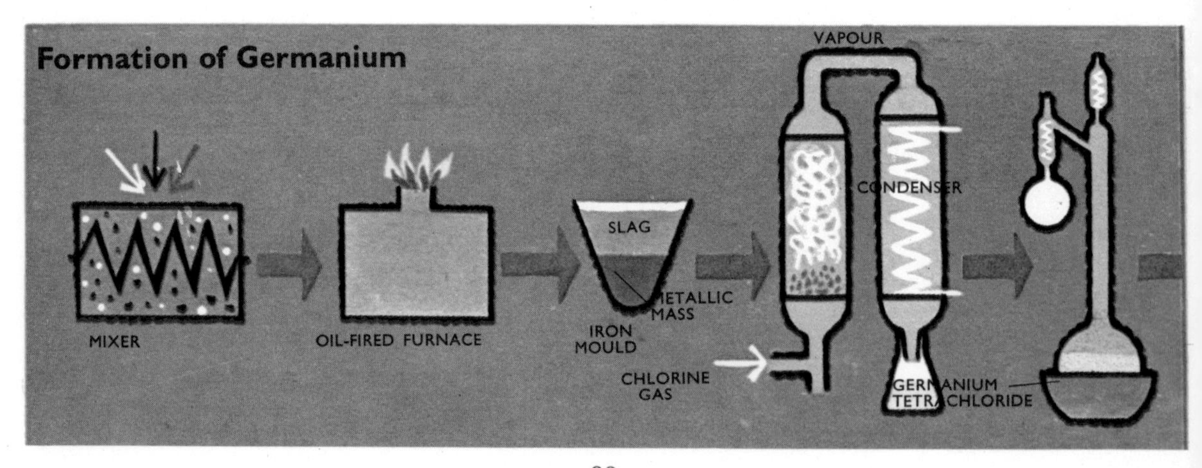

130°C.) by fractional distillation.

The purified germanium tetrachloride is then converted to germanium dioxide by hydrolysis with water:

$$\underset{\text{germanium tetrachloride}}{GeCl_4} + \underset{\text{water}}{2H_2O} \rightarrow \underset{\text{germanium dioxide}}{GeO_2} + \underset{\text{hydrochloric acid}}{4HCl}$$

After filtration the germanium dioxide powder is heated in a stream of hydrogen gas and is thereby reduced to germanium metal.

However, for transistors to work satisfactorily the germanium must be of a high state of purity, and to achieve this further refining is necessary, and this is done by the *zone refining* technique. In this a narrow zone of the metal ingot is heated to its melting point (958°C.) using a high-frequency coil. The heating coil moves slowly along the length of the ingot, melting the narrow zone as it does so. Pure germanium crystallizes when the coil has passed, while the impurities tend to become concentrated in the molten zone which migrates towards one end as the heating coil traverses the ingot. After passing the germanium bar through the coil several times a specimen of very high purity is obtained. It takes about 7 hours to purify 2 kg. (4½ lb.) of germanium by this method, and in doing so it has to be passed through six heating zones.

Germanium is a grey-white crystalline solid with a metallic lustre. It is unaffected by hydrochloric acid, dilute sulphuric acid or concentrated sodium hydroxide solution. However, it does react with concentrated nitric acid and with dilute sodium hydroxide solution. Sodium germanate (Na_2GeO_3) is formed when germanium reacts with fused sodium hydroxide. Germanium forms two series of compounds—the german*ous*, in which it has a valency of *two*, and the german*ic*, with a valency of *four*. In this way it resembles tin which also forms two series of compounds.

There are two oxides of germanium and both of them are *amphoteric*—they behave both as acidic and basic oxides. Germanium also forms a series of hydrides which resemble the hydrides of silicon (the silanes).

As already stated, the principal use of germanium is in electronic devices such as rectifiers and transistors. Germanium has a crystal structure similar to that of diamond—the four valency bonds are linked one to each of the four nearest germanium atoms. Very pure germanium is a poor conductor

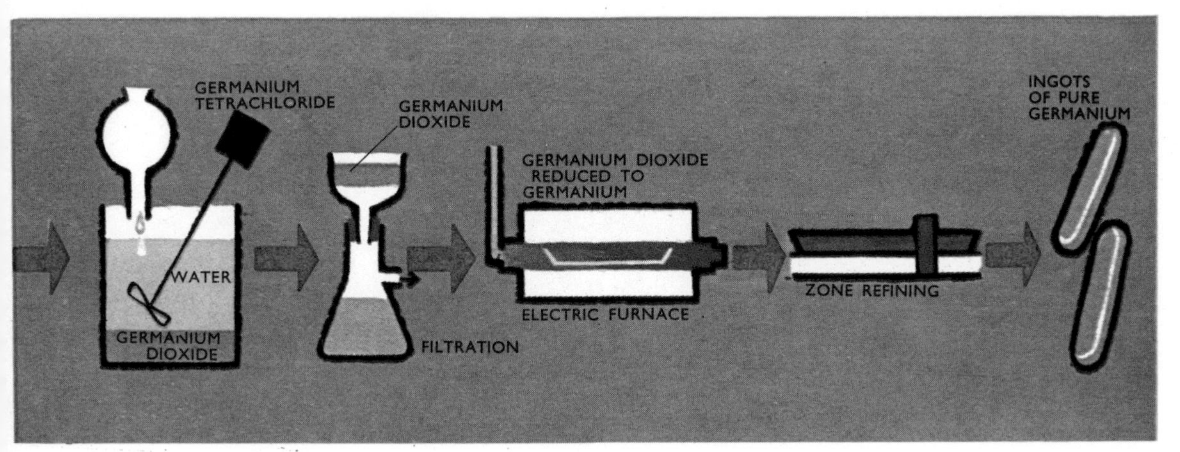

of electricity, but if traces of trivalent or pentavalent elements (e.g. indium or arsenic) are added the conductivity is increased.

If a small quantity of a pentavalent metal like arsenic or antimony is added, the arsenic or antimony atoms replace a few germanium atoms in the crystal lattice. These atoms of impurity contribute five valency electrons compared with four from each germanium atom, so there is a spare electron available for current carrying associated with each atom of impurity. As there is then a free *negative* charge the product is known as *n*-type germanium.

When traces of aluminium or indium are added there will be an electron deficiency (or 'hole') surrounding each trivalent atom. This will also assist the flow of electrons which constitutes an electric current. The germanium is then *p*-type since the electron deficiency is equivalent to a free *positive* charge.

A small piece of each type (*n* and *p*) of germanium when pressed together have similar rectifying properties to diode valves and only permit electrons to flow in one direction. However, if one type is 'sandwiched' between two pieces of the other type a device similar in characteristics to a triode valve is obtained. The latter semi-conductor devices are known as *transistors*.

Not only are germanium rectifiers used as radio and television components, they are also used in power rectifiers for electric traction. A number of locomotives which incorporate germanium rectifiers have been undergoing trials.

Magnesium germanate ($MgGeO_3$) is used in the coatings of fluorescent lamps to add red to the light emitted. A gold-germanium alloy (88% : 12%) is used as a solder in electronic devices, while the strength of aluminium alloys can be improved by adding germanium to them.

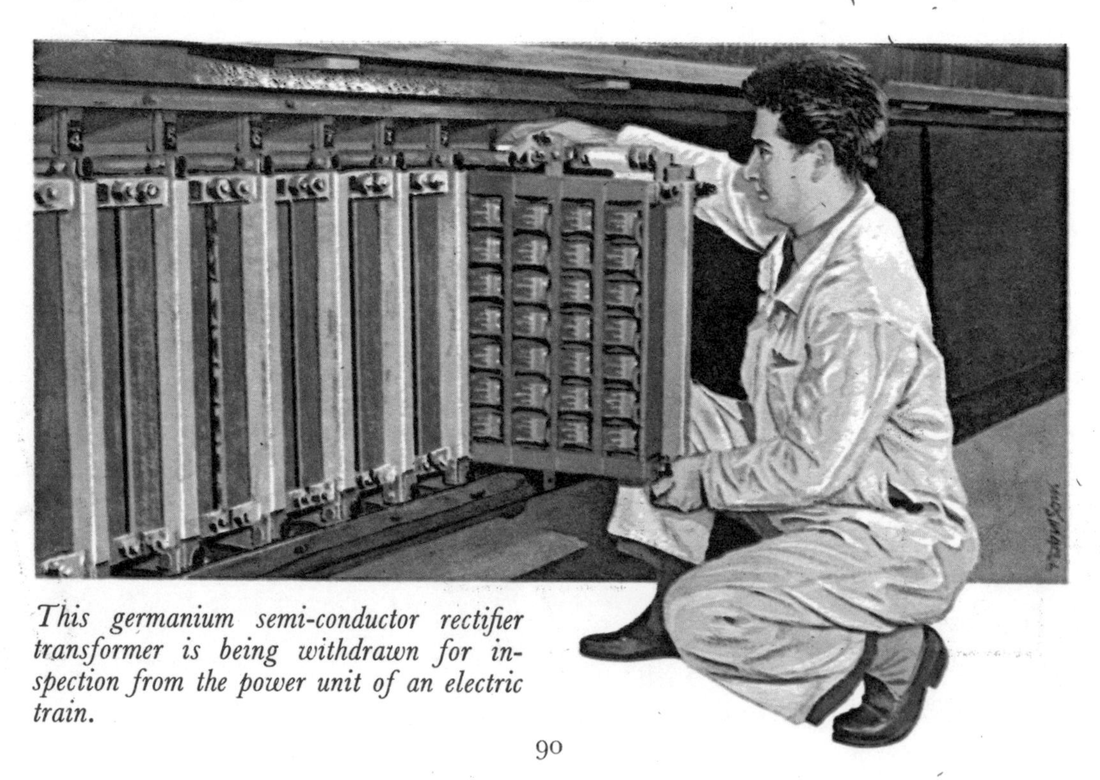

This germanium semi-conductor rectifier transformer is being withdrawn for inspection from the power unit of an electric train.

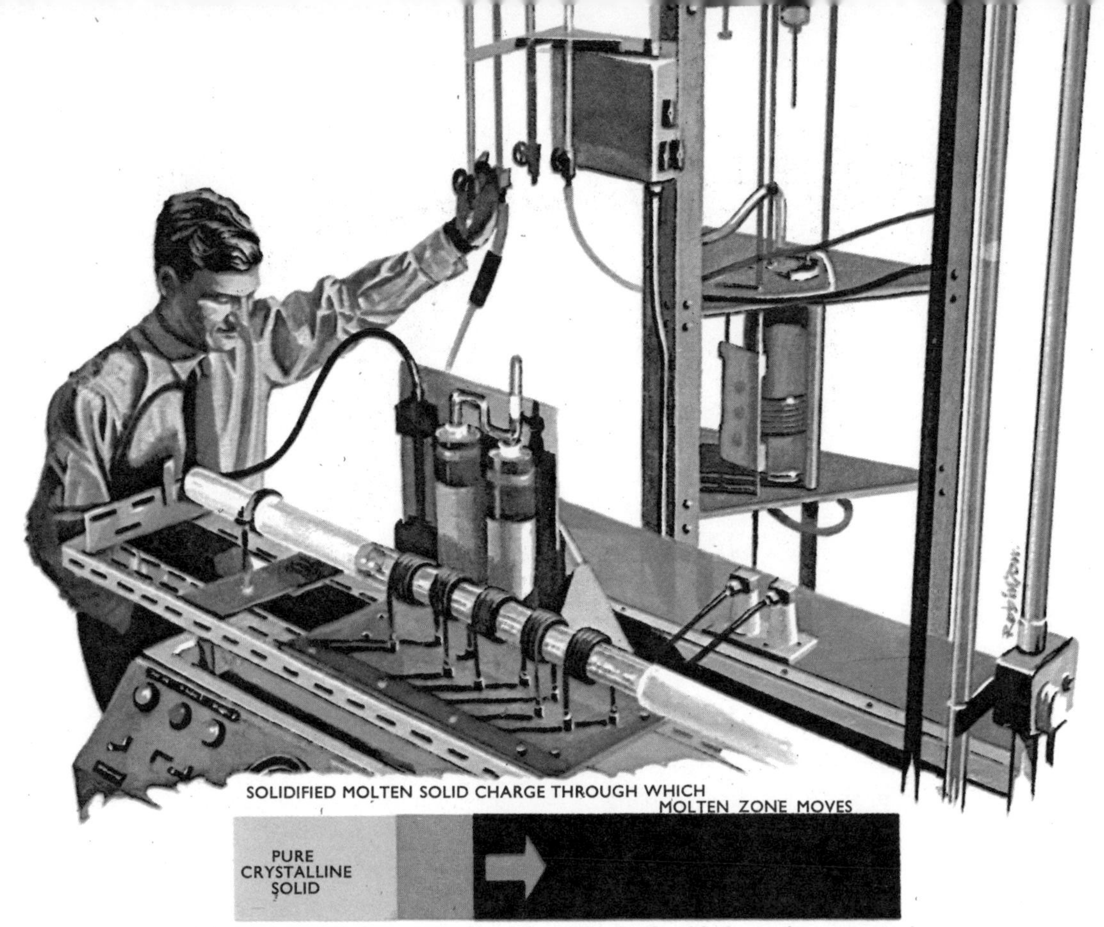

The zone refining technique by which the high purity germanium needed in electronic devices is finally obtained. The impurities become concentrated in the narrow band of molten metal which slowly traverses the germanium ingot.

Tin

No one knows where tin was first mined and extracted but it was probably in use thousands of years before the birth of Christ. At any rate, it was certainly among the first metals to be extracted. This was done very simply by placing lumps of its ore in a charcoal fire and collecting the tin as it trickled out at the bottom. The tin mines of Cornwall were once so famous that the British Isles were known as the Cassiterides (the Tin Islands). But these mines have long fallen into disuse. Now, Malaya is the principal producer with Indonesia and Bolivia each producing about half as much ore.

Tin is a white shiny metal with a slightly bluish tinge. Compared with most other metals it is soft, so soft in fact that it can be cut with a knife. Vessels made of pure tin are easily knocked out of shape, but alloys made of copper and tin are hard, harder than pure copper. The discovery of the copper/tin alloy, *bronze*, changed the whole course of civilization. Nowadays, tin is alloyed with other metals or used as a protective coating.

The ore, *tinstone* or *cassiterite*, is the sole source of commercial tin. It contains stannic oxide SnO_2, and is dark brown in colour. The tinstone is first crushed and then the unwanted

Separation of tin ore from crushed tin-bearing material. The ore sinks to the bottom of the water and collects behind wooden slats.

earthy material is removed from it. As the oxide is about seven times as dense as water, it sinks to the bottom of a fast-flowing stream while the earth is washed on. (This is rather similar in principle to panning for gold.) The ore concentrate contains impurities of arsenic and sulphur. These are removed by roasting in the presence of air. The impurities are changed to oxides and blown away as gases.

The next stage is to remove the oxygen from the stannic oxide so that only the metallic tin remains. Carbon in the form of anthracite is used as the reducing agent. It combines with the oxygen becoming carbon dioxide

$$SnO_2 + C \rightarrow Sn + CO_2$$

stannic oxide, carbon, tin, carbon dioxide

The furnace is stacked with roasted ore, anthracite and limestone. The slag floats and the tin sinks to the bottom where it is drawn off in the molten state to solidify as ingots which

The tin ore is mixed with limestone and anthracite ready for smelting.

Smelting furnace in operation. The technical manager wears dark glasses so that he can look into the white-hot mass inside.

are 99·5% tin. The slag is processed to remove any remaining tin and the tin is then *refined* to remove most impurities. It is heated until it just melts and poured down a slope built of firebricks. The flowing liquid is stirred with poles of green wood. This prevents the tin from oxidizing and gas bubbles rising from the charring wood bring the impurities to the surface. Purified tin collects at the bottom and the dross is left at the top. Tin can also be refined by electrolysis.

A certain amount of tin is recovered from old tinplate such as old tin cans. These cans are in fact made of steel coated very thinly with tin. The cans are cleaned to remove grease and treated with chlorine which converts the tin into stannic chloride from which the tin can be recovered. Alternatively the stannic chloride can be used direct for giving body and weight to pure silk. This makes it handle well. The silk retains about 40% of the chloride.

Chemistry of Tin

In dry air, tin stays bright and does not corrode but a very thin invisible layer of oxide does in fact form on the surface. It is possible to remove this layer by attacking the underlying tin with iodine vapour. Very strong heating of tin produces a visible oxide layer.

Under ordinary conditions tin is not attacked by water although in the molten state steam at 800°C oxidizes it to stannic oxide SnO_2. Because of this high stability tin is good for lining water stills, geysers, electric kettles, etc.

The halogens, chlorine, bromine and iodine all attack tin, forming halides. For example, with chlorine the product is stannic chloride.

$$\underset{\text{tin}}{Sn} + \underset{\text{chlorine}}{2Cl_2} \rightarrow \underset{\text{stannic chloride}}{SnCl_4}$$

Tin has two possible valencies, 2

The object has been plated by dipping it in molten tin.

Soldering a header tank to the radiator of a car. (Solder is an alloy of tin and lead.)

and 4. This gives rise to two series of compounds, stann*ous* compounds (*e.g.* stann*ous* chloride $SnCl_2$), where tin has a valency of 2, and stann*ic* compounds (*e.g.* stann*ic* chloride $SnCl_4$) where the valency is 4. The stann*ic* series is the more stable.

Tin reacts with acids to form salts. There is no reaction with cold dilute acids. They must be hot and concentrated. With concentrated hydrochloric acid, stann*ous* chloride is formed but with nitric and sulphuric acids the stann*ic* salts are formed.

Tin is attacked by alkalis forming solutions of *stannates* and hydrogen is given off. With sodium hydroxide, sodium stannate, Na_2SnO_3, is formed. Therefore alkalis are not suitable for cleaning tinware.

Although tin is usually thought of as being silvery and shiny, this is not always the case, for tin can exist in three different crystalline forms (*allotropes*). Each allotrope has a range of temperature in which it is stable and the others are unstable. The silvery *white* shiny *tin* is stable between 13°C and about 180°C. When this tin is bent it emits a painful sounding cry caused by its crystals rubbing together. Above 180°C, *rhombic tin* is stable. Below 13°C the stable allotrope is a dull *grey* powdery form of tin. This does not mean that when tin is cooled to below 13°C there is a rapid crumble. The transformation is very slow indeed and the tin must often be kept at this temperature for months before the change begins. Once started though, the spread is rapid. The transition is known as *tin plague*. After one very severe winter in Leningrad, a whole cellar of tin bullion was changed into grey dust, but this is unusual. The crystal structure is shattered and a 25% increase of volume takes place with the change.

Uses of tin

Most tin is used for plating other metals such as steel. The tinplate is largely used by the foodstuffs industry because tin does not contaminate the food. Cans are plated with tin; milk vats and pipes along which food passes are tin-lined. Nowadays most plating is done by electrolysis in plastic-lined tanks. The object being plated is made the cathode and the anode is of tin. Both anode and cathode dip in a solution of a stannous or stannic compound. The other method is by hot dipping. Here, the object is dipped for a few seconds into molten tin. The tin has a very good wetting power and forms a thin film on the surface (often only ·00003 in. thick). Tin is a very weak metal and when pushed out of shape does not spring back. For this reason it is used to make tubes for artists' colours. Plastic tubes would open out again drawing air into the tube. Tin foil is used for wrapping because it has no tendency to open out.

The next largest use of tin is for alloying with other metals. Solder is an alloy of tin and lead (fine solder is 66% tin and 34% lead). Gunmetal and bronze are largely copper with a small percentage of tin. Pewter is tin hardened with lead. It is a very good alloy for ornamental work and jewellery.

Old coins with tin plague.

The importance of organo-tin compounds is on the increase. In them, an atom of tin is joined to one or two atoms of carbon. They are used to protect the plastic polyvinyl chloride (P.V.C.) against discoloration. Stannous chloride is added to soap to prevent it from discolouring and losing its perfume. Stannic oxide is used to give a cloudy look to glazes and enamels.

USES OF TIN

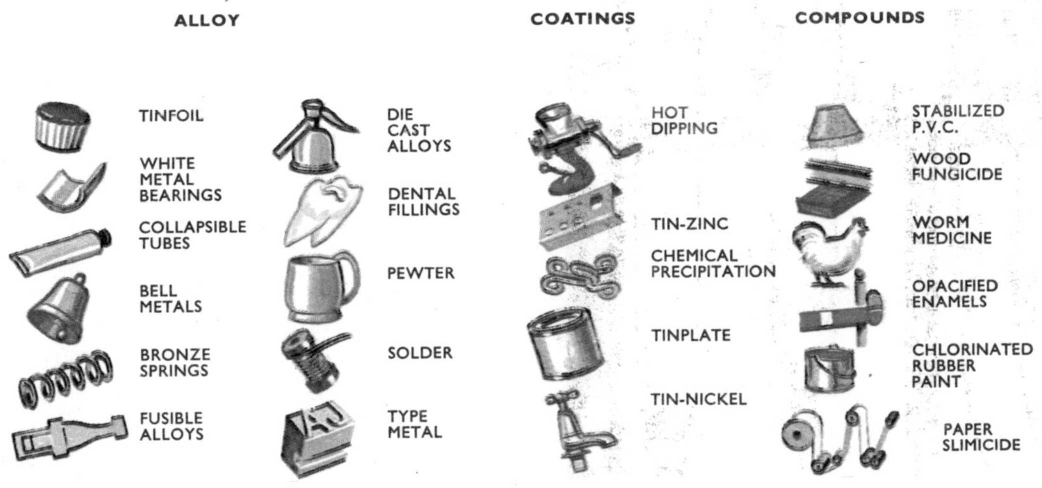

Lead forms only about 0·002% of the Earth's crust. Occasionally small quantities of lead crystals are found, but it mostly occurs in combination with other elements. *Galena* (lead sulphide PbS) is the commonest ore and most of the world's lead is extracted from it. The less common ores, *cerussite* (lead carbonate, $PbCO_3$) and *anglesite* (lead sulphate, $PbSO_4$) can also be used. The important producers of lead from galena ore are the United States, Mexico, Australia and Canada. About 2,000,000 tons of lead are produced annually. A considerable amount of this is reclaimed scrap lead.

Because it is very resistant to corrosion, and soft and pliable, making it easy to work, lead has long been in use for making water pipes. The Ancient Egyptians, Romans and early Britons all used it for their piping, and lead is still in great demand for this purpose.

Lead covered cables in the basement of a modern telephone exchange.

Although better grade ore is preferred, galena deposits containing as little as 3% lead sulphide can be profitably worked. After mining, the rock bearing the galena is brought to the surface and crushed to a powder. The lead-bearing ore is separated from the useless rock by *froth-flotation*. Violent gusts of air are blown through a stream of water to which a small amount of pine oil has been added. The air keeps the water in constant motion. The unwanted rock sinks to the bottom, but the ore is borne to the surface in a froth of bubbles. The froth is skimmed off the top and dried, forming a *concentrate*.

The concentrate is then *roasted*. This is a process for removing most of the sulphur. During roasting, the temperature is kept well below the melting point of the sulphide ore. Air is blown in. Part of the sulphide is oxidized to lead oxide and part to lead sulphate.

$$2PbS + 3O_2 \rightarrow 2PbO + 2SO_2$$

2PbS	+	3O₂	→	2PbO	+	2SO₂
lead sulphide		oxygen		lead oxide		sulphur dioxide

$$PbS + 2O_2 \rightarrow PbSO_4$$

PbS	+	2O₂	→	PbSO₄
lead sulphide		oxygen		lead sulphate

Some flux is added to the fine powder from the roasting to make it into coarser lumps. The fine powder would otherwise choke the *blast furnace*. The furnace is charged with roasted ore, coke, limestone and some scrap iron to remove any remaining sulphur. The carbon in the coke removes the oxygen as oxides. The molten lead is run off from the bottom.

Sometimes lead ores are found intermingled with those of zinc. Here, the treatment is different. The two ores are treated as one. This method is described in the article on zinc.

After smelting, the lead contains many impurities such as antimony, arsenic, bismuth, copper, silver, gold, tin and zinc. Consequently further *refining* is necessary. There are a number of alternative ways of doing this to obtain very pure lead.

Lead is a bluish grey metal. When its surface is scraped with a penknife, it has quite a bright shine. Air quickly tarnishes it into dullness, but the action of the air does not make it crumble away. It only gives it a coating which acts as a protection against further action with the air.

Lead is a weighty, dense metal. At 20°C its density is 11·34 gm/cc, over 11 times as dense as water. The atomic weight of lead is 207·2. In a block of lead, the atoms are arranged in a face centred cubic structure. The building unit is a cube with a lead atom at each corner and one at the middle of each side.

Lead is a soft metal which is quite easy to cut with a knife and can easily be bent out of shape. When a bead of lead is rubbed across a piece of paper, some of the atoms rub off and a greyish black mark is left on the paper. At one time lead was used for making pencils.

Lead is fairly resistant to acid attack. Dilute sulphuric and hydrochloric acids do not affect it, but nitric acid does.

The lead in most lead compounds has a valency of *two* although it can

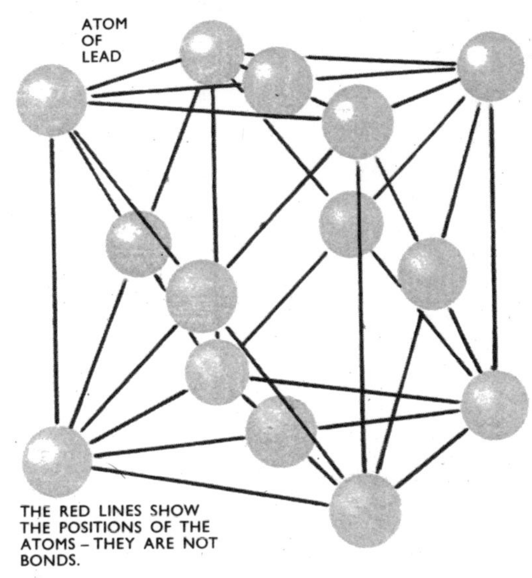

The atoms in solid lead are arranged in this face centred cubic structure.

also have other valencies. For example, lead forms several oxides. In *litharge* (lead monoxide, PbO) the lead has a valency of two. Litharge is a pale yellow powder used in preparing oils and varnishes and is sometimes added to flint glass to increase its refractive index. It will react with both acids and alkalies and is therefore called an *amphoteric* oxide. The chocolate coloured lead dioxide, (PbO_2), is made by oxidizing lead in an alkaline solution. Here, the lead has a valency of four. In each molecule, one atom of lead has combined with two atoms of oxygen of valency two. The red lead used in paints has the formula Pb_3O_4. Other oxides of lead are the *suboxide* Pb_2O and the *sesquioxide*, Pb_2O_3.

In most lead compounds other than the oxides the lead is divalent. For example, when alkalies are added to solutions of lead salts it is always white lead hydroxide, $Pb(OH)_2$ (divalent lead) that is precipitated. Like litharge the hydroxide is amphoteric and will react with both acids and alkalies. When an excess of alkali is added, the precipitated hydroxide dissolves.

Lead compounds are well known for their insolubility in water. Lead nitrate and lead acetate are two exceptions, but unlike many sulphates, lead sulphate is insoluble.

Great care must be taken in handling lead compounds because they are very poisonous. The poison is cumulative because the elimination via the kidneys is very slow.

Industrially, the most important lead compound is lead tetra-ethyl. Small amounts of this liquid are added to motor fuel as an anti-knock to increase the efficiency of the engine.

Most of the 2,000,000 tons annual consumption of lead is used in the metallic form, not as its compounds. Sheets of lead are used for roofing, in particular for protecting awkward joints where the water might seep in. Because of its large atomic weight, lead is an excellent absorber of X and gamma rays. Thick slabs of lead are used by workers handling radioactive materials to protect them from the harmful effects of radiation. For protection against X-rays the lead may be only a few millimetres thick, but for strong gamma rays it may be several inches thick.

Lead piping is made in a very interesting manner. Hot solid lead is forced through an aperture called a *die*. In the centre of this hole is a steel rod. The lead is forced through the hole to form a hollow pipe. A similar method is used for giving telephone and power cables a protective lead sheathing.

Most cars have a lead accumulator or battery. The positive plate is made of lead dioxide and the negative plate of spongy lead.

In the alloy form, lead is used together with tin to make solder. The exact composition depends on the type of solder required.

Radio-isotopes being handled by remote control. Blocks of lead shield the man from their harmful radiation, and the glass is made with a high content of lead oxide.

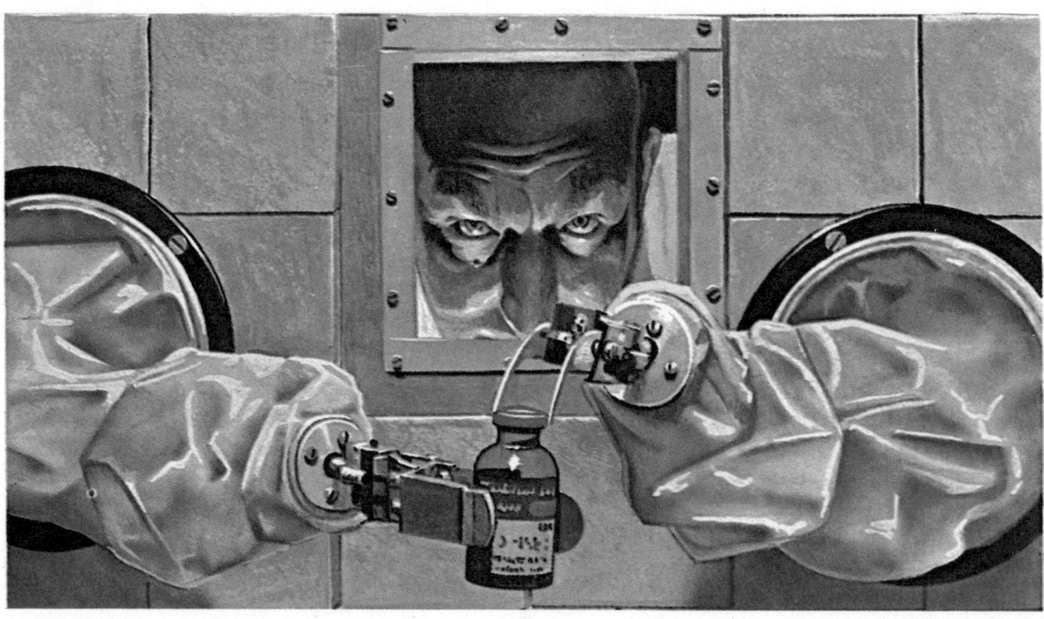

CHAPTER EIGHT

Group 5

NITROGEN

Whereas substances will burst into flame when put in oxygen, nitrogen does not assist burning. The compounds of nitrogen are chemically reactive although the element itself is rather unreactive. Nitrogen combines directly with only a few elements, such as magnesium. If magnesium is heated in pure nitrogen, magnesium nitride is formed. In fact, when magnesium is burnt in air, a small quantity of the magnesium reacts with the nitrogen of the air to form magnesium nitride while the bulk of the magnesium combines with oxygen to give magnesium oxide.

The Earth's atmosphere is composed of about one-fifth oxygen and four-fifths nitrogen, and both these gases are obtained on an industrial scale by *fractional distillation* of liquid air. After removing the small quantities of water vapour and carbon dioxide which are always present, the air is liquefied. This is achieved by a combination of cooling and expansion.

In the *Claude process* air is compressed until its pressure is about 40 times that of the atmosphere and as a result heat is generated. This heat is removed by the cold air which has not been liquefied and the fresh gas is cooled to *minus* 70°C. Some of the cool air is then allowed to expand to atmospheric pressure. This process takes heat from the air itself and as a

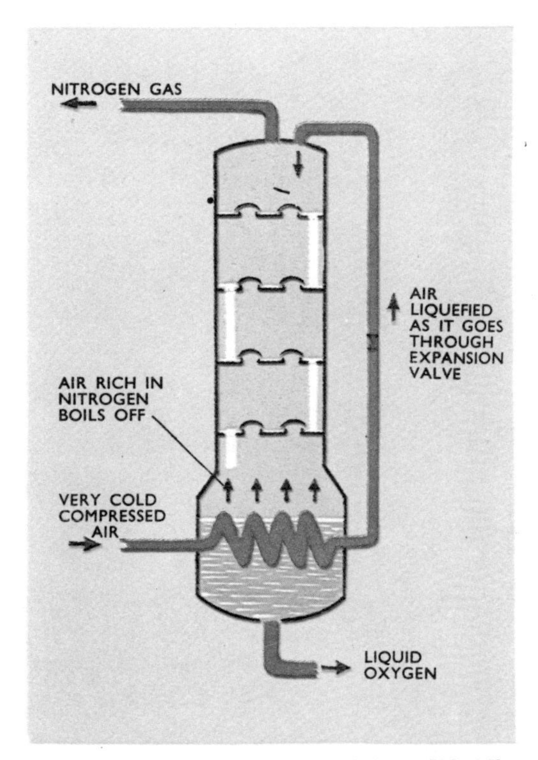

A Rectification column (simplified) for separation of oxygen and nitrogen: *When liquid air comes into contact with cool gaseous air, nitrogen gas tends to boil off, while oxygen collects in the liquid. The liquid air is fed in at the top of the column, while the liquid which collects at the bottom is boiled. (The heat remaining in the cool gaseous air is sufficient to cause boiling, and at the same time the gaseous air is still further cooled.) These two streams are mixed on successive plates so that almost pure nitrogen gas can be taken from the top of the column, while liquid oxygen can be removed from the base.*

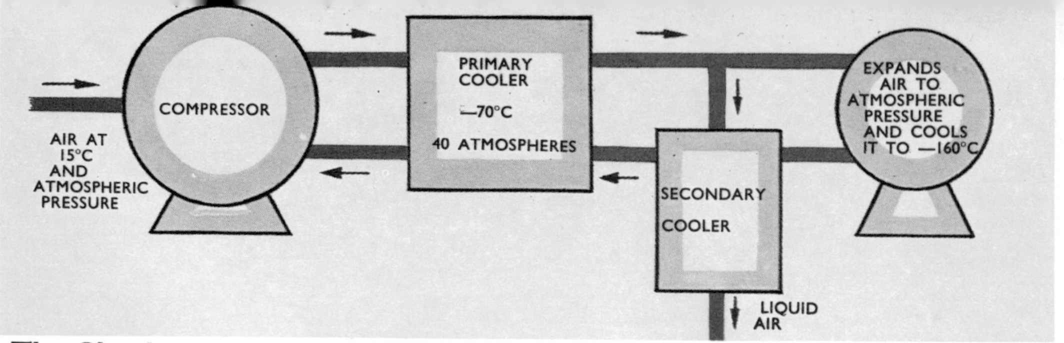

The Claude process for liquefaction of air: *Note how the gas which has not been liquefied is first used to cool the compressed air which is at – 70 °C (in the Secondary Cooler). The gas which is being re-circulated is still cold enough to take the heat out of the freshly compressed air. In the Primary Cooler, this compressed air is cooled to – 70 °C.*

result the air is still further cooled to *minus* 160 °C. The air remaining at high pressure is cooled sufficiently by the air which has expanded so that the air at high pressure is turned to liquid.

Once the gases of the air have been liquefied it is possible to separate the nitrogen from the oxygen because they each turn back into gases (*i.e.* boil) at a different temperature. So at an exactly controlled temperature nitrogen will turn into a gas (above – 196 °C), while at that temperature (and below – 183 °C) oxygen still remains a liquid. The method of boiling the liquid air is to let it fall to the bottom of the rectification column down to the coiled tube that brings in the cold air as a gas. This is comparatively much warmer than the liquid air, which therefore boils. All the nitrogen turns to gas and rises to the top to be collected. Unfortunately some of the oxygen in the liquid air also boils, but it has a strong tendency to condense again. It is made to do so on the perforated plates down which the very cold liquid air is flowing, and liquid oxygen joins the liquid air going downwards. Very soon the liquid at the bottom of this tower is almost only liquid oxygen, and only pure nitrogen rises to the top.

The fountain experiment: *So great is the solubility of ammonia in water that a partial vacuum is created in the flask containing ammonia gas because so much ammonia goes into the water. Water is, therefore, sucked up into the flask. If red litmus is added to the water in the beaker, the colour of the solution is changed to blue as soon as the ammonia dissolves. This shows that ammonia is a base.*

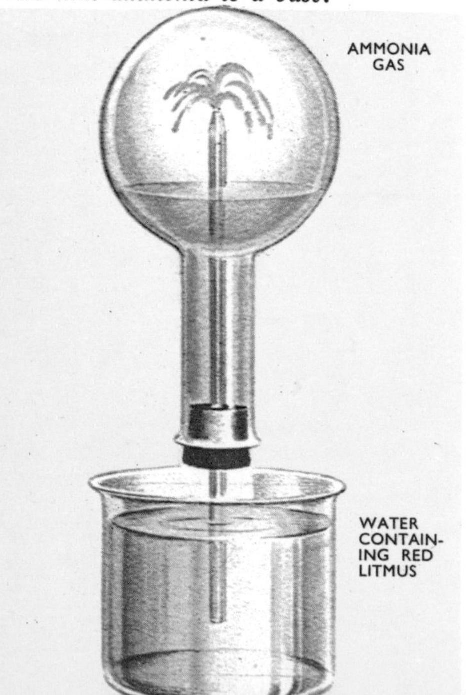

Compounds of Nitrogen

Nitrogen in combination with other elements is widely distributed in Nature: nitrogen is a constituent of many very important compounds, including explosives such as T.N.T., drugs and various dyes.

Proteins make up the greater part of the solid matter of all animal cells and tissues and are present in various

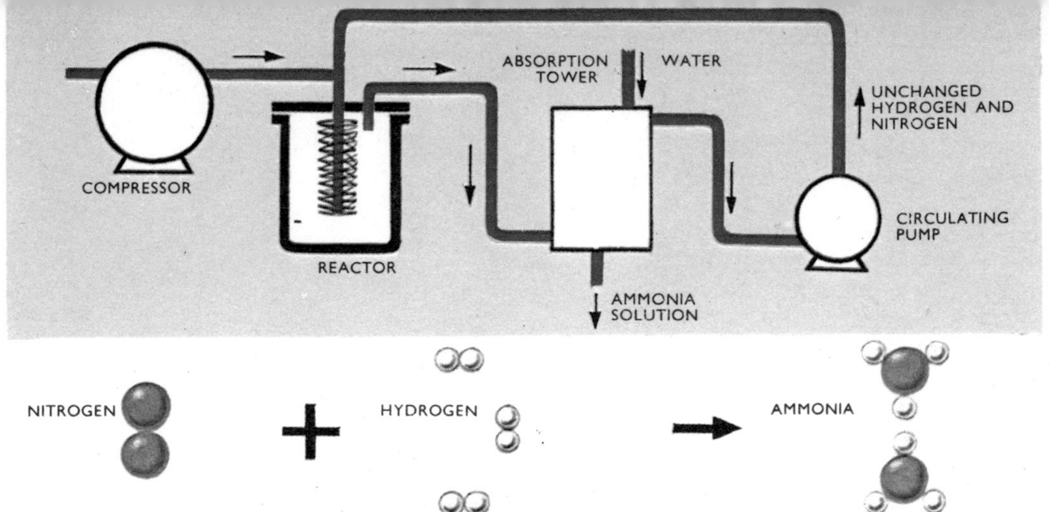

Synthesis of ammonia: *Some of the hydrogen and nitrogen react together to form ammonia which is dissolved in water in the absorption tower. The unchanged hydrogen and nitrogen is re-circulated.*

parts of plants. Meat and eggs consist mainly of protein: milk, seeds and some fruits also contain a high proportion of it. Proteins are rather complex in nature, but all contain on an average 16 per cent of nitrogen.

In combination with hydrogen and oxygen, nitrogen gives rise to nitrous acid (HNO_2) and nitric acid (HNO_3). The salts of nitric acid, the *nitrates*, are fairly abundant, and extensive deposits of sodium nitrate, which is more commonly known as Chile saltpetre, occur in Chile.

Another important compound of nitrogen is the base, *ammonia* (NH_3). There are traces of this gas in the air and derivatives of ammonia occur in plants and animals (e.g. in blood and urine), in the soil and in certain natural waters. Ammonia is formed when organic matter containing nitrogen decomposes.

Ammonia and ammonium salts are present in *gas-liquor* which is obtained as a by-product in the manufacture of coal gas and coke. This source of ammonia gas is now comparatively unimportant. It is made in much larger quantities by synthesis (*i.e.* building it up) from hydrogen and atmospheric nitrogen.

The mixture of hydrogen and nitrogen gases, in the correct proportions for the reaction (*i.e.* three times as much hydrogen as nitrogen) is compressed and passed rapidly over heated iron grids in the reactor. Some of the gases in the mixture combine to give another gas, ammonia. Being a gas the ammonia leaving the reactor has, of course, to be separated from the hydrogen and nitrogen which have not combined. This is fairly easily done as ammonia is very soluble in water while hydrogen and nitrogen are not.

The iron grids in the reaction chamber do not undergo any permanent chemical change, although their presence in the reactor is essential to the synthesis. Any such substance which helps to bring about a chemical change without itself undergoing permanent chemical change in the reaction is known as a *catalyst*.

Ammonia is a colourless gas with a strong, biting smell. It is lighter than air—it can be poured upwards. The gas does not burn in air, neither does it permit burning. However, if a burning taper is dipped into a jar of the gas, the flame of the taper is surrounded for a short time by a large greenish-yellow flame This is

HYDROGEN CHLORIDE
AMMONIA
AMMONIUM CHLORIDE

The two colourless gases, ammonia and hydrogen chloride, react to form a white cloud of ammonium chloride, which is really a solid.

caused by the decomposition of ammonia into nitrogen and hydrogen.

Ammonia is very soluble in water—this is shown in a most striking way by the 'fountain experiment'—and household ammonia, which is used to soften water used for laundering, is a solution of the gas in water. This solution is alkaline - it turns red litmus blue - and reacts with acids to form the ammonium series of salts.

If a jar of the colourless gas hydrogen chloride (a solution of this is called hydrochloric acid) is placed on top of a jar of ammonia, and the dividing disc is removed, a white cloud of ammonium chloride is formed. This is subsequently deposited as a white powder on the walls of the jars.

Ammonium sulphate is probably the most important ammonium salt as it is widely used in agriculture as a nitrogen-containing fertilizer. It is usually made from ammonia and

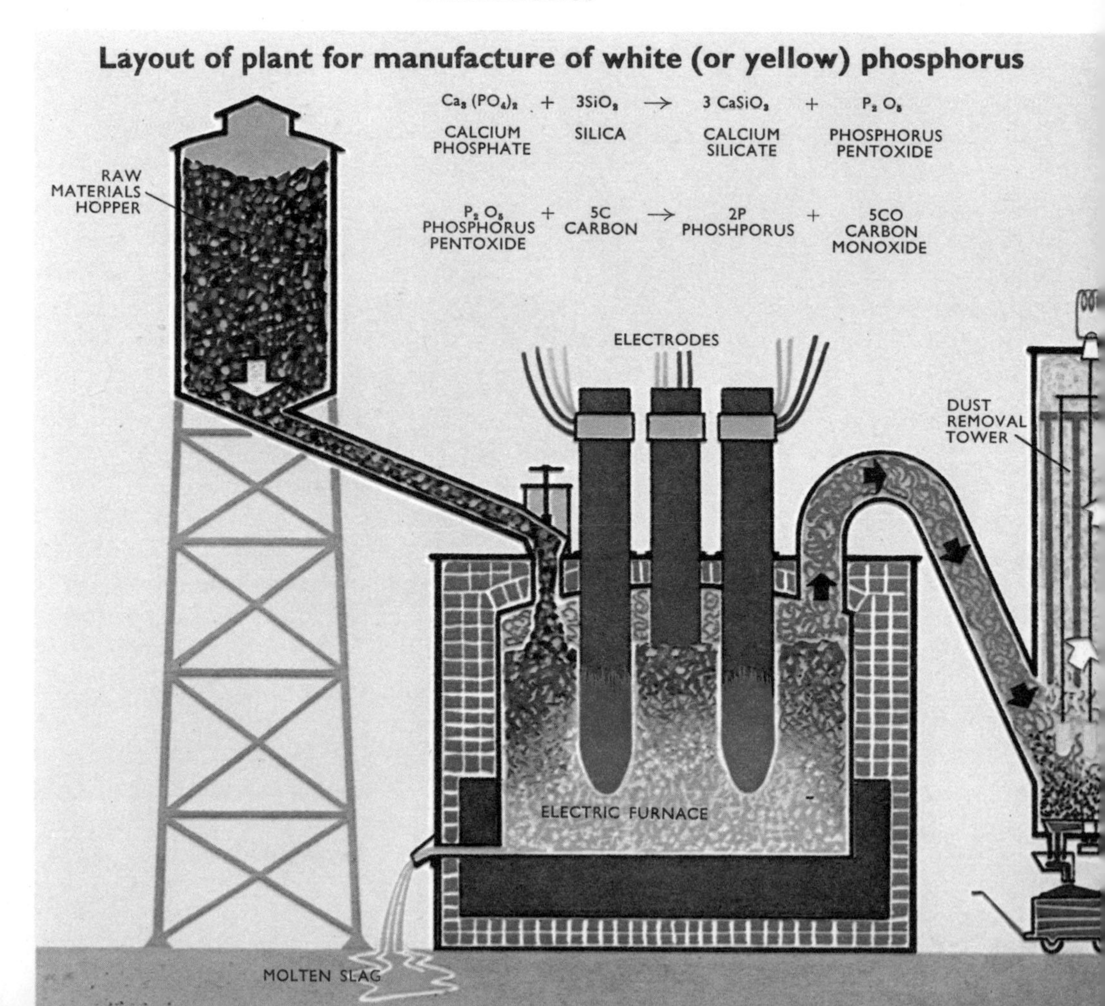

sulphuric acid.

The element phosphorus exists in several different forms (*allotropes*)—white (or yellow) phosphorus is highly inflammable and poisonous, while red phosphorus is less poisonous and only burns when heated. Although these two allotropes have such different physical properties, the compounds formed from them are identical. Thus phosphorus pentoxide may be obtained by burning either the white or the red form in air.

The phosphoric acids which are obtained when phosphorus pentoxide reacts with water, give rise to several series of salts—the phosphates. The latter provide an important storehouse of energy in plant and animal cells. Red phosphorus (the element) is also used in making matches.

Phosphorus is such a reactive element that it is only found in a combined state in nature. The principal commercial source is phosphate rock or fluorapatite, $3Ca_3(PO_4)_2.CaF_2$, also chlorapatite $3Ca_3(PO_4)_2.CaCl_2$. Bone-ash, which is obtained by roasting bones, was formerly used as a source of phosphorus: bone-ash contains about 80% calcium phosphate.

The modern method of manufacturing phosphorus is to heat phosphate rock with a mixture of sand (or quartz) and coke in an electric furnace to a temperature of 1500°C. The extraction of the phosphorus from the calcium phosphate in the phosphate rock takes place in two stages. In the first phosphorus pentoxide vapour and calcium silicate are formed by a reaction between the calcium phosphate and silica (sand). The calcium silicate forms a molten slag which can periodically be withdrawn from the base of the furnace.

In a second reaction carbon (coke) reacts with the phosphorus pentoxide vapour—carbon monoxide and phosphorous vapour are formed (Carbon acts as a *reducing* agent and is itself *oxidised* to carbon monoxide) The phosphorous vapour together with the carbon monoxide rise out of the top of the furnace, and any dust particles in the furnace gases are removed. The dust-free gases then enter a series of condensers. The phosphorous vapour is condensed (turned to liquid) by spraying with warm water—the liquid phosphorus is stored under water.

The furnace which has fire-brick walls and a carbon hearth, is heated by the electric arcs which are struck between the three electrodes sus-

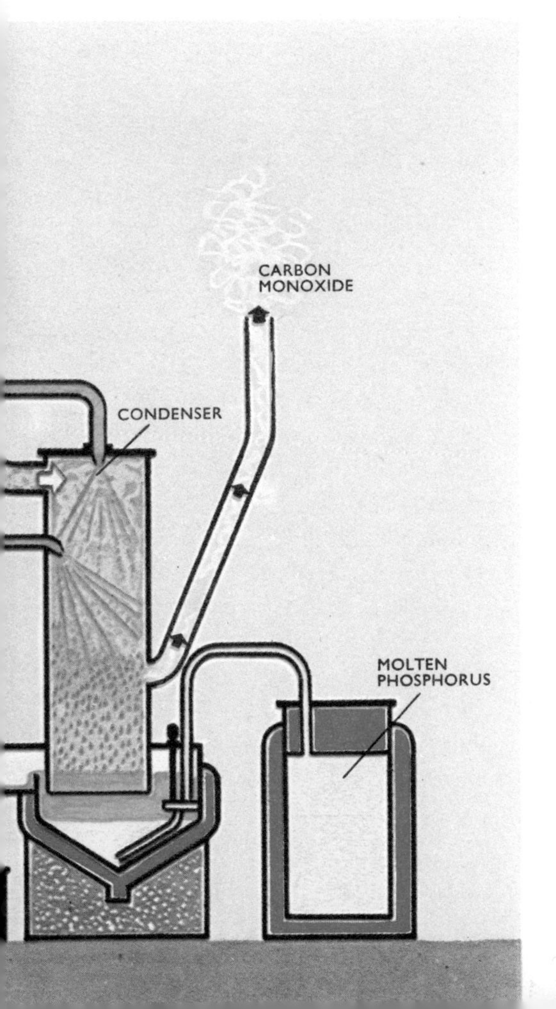

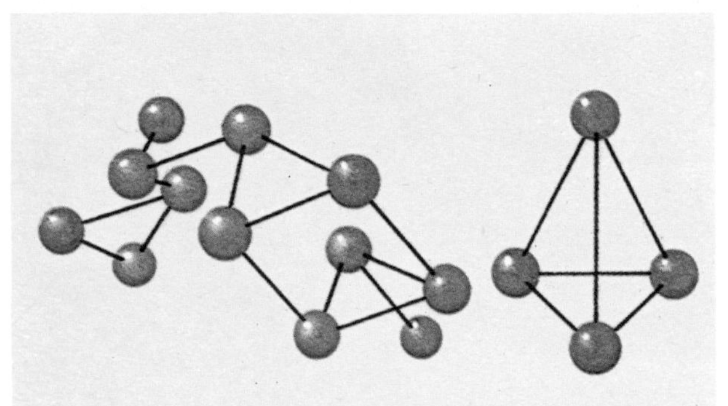

Structure of red phosphorus (*left*) and white or yellow phosphorus (*right*). Molecules of the yellow allotrope are simpler and more reactive.

pended from the roof of the furnace. In this process the electric current is being used as a source of *heat*: the same series of chemical reaction were formerly carried out in the older blast furnace process in which the heat needed for the reactions was obtained by burning some of the coke with the aid of a blast of air.

These methods of preparation all yield the poisonous white allotrope. If red phosphorus is required, this can be obtained by heating the white variety for several days at a temperature of 270°C. On account of the risk of explosion, the heating has to be carried out with great care. The white allotrope is placed in a cast iron or steel pot with a close-fitting lid which incorporates a safety pipe. Air is excluded from the pot. After four or five days, the temperature of the pot is raised to 400°C in order that unchanged white phosphorus may be distilled off. After cooling, the hard red cake left in the pot is ground under water and then boiled with caustic soda to remove any residual white phosphorus. The red allotrope is finally washed with hot water, filtered and dried under vacuum.

White phosphorus, an almost transparent wax-like solid, burns so readily that it is usually stored under water in which it does not dissolve. Furthermore, the warmth of the hand is sufficient to set this allotrope alight. For this reason it should always be handled with forceps and never with bare fingers. White phosphorus is soluble in carbon disulphide. If a sheet of filter paper (or blotting paper) is soaked in such a solution and the solvent (carbon disulphide) allowed to evaporate, the very small phosphorous particles deposited on the paper oxidize so rapidly that the paper bursts into flame by itself. White phosphorus reacts with a hot concentrated solution of sodium hydroxide (caustic soda) and poisonous phosphine gas is formed.

By contrast red phosphorus is much less reactive than the white form. The red allotrope has to be *heated* in air to a temperature of 260°C before it will burn. The product of the combustion is the same compound—phosphorus pentoxide—as is obtained when white phosphorus burns in air. The red variety is not soluble in carbon disulphide, neither does it react with hot concentrated solutions of sodium hydroxide.

In the solid state the atoms of phosphorus in the white allotrope are arranged in triangular pyramids. There are four atoms in each molecule one situated at each corner of the pyramid—and each atom in the molecule is joined to the other three by single bonds. However, the structure of the red form is rather more complicated. Each phosphorous atom is still linked to three neighbouring atoms by single bonds. Instead of the atoms being grouped together in small units, they are arranged in a much larger mass. The contrasting properties of the two allotropes may be attributed to their different structures.

The two important oxides of phosphorus are phosphorus trioxide and phosphorus pentoxide. Both are obtained when phosphorus is burned in air—if the supply of air is restricted the trioxide is formed, while if there is an excess of air the pentoxide is obtained. Phosphorus trioxide is a crystalline solid which melts at 22·5°C. If exposed in the air it slowly oxidizes to the pentoxide. The pentoxide is a white solid which absorbs moisture from the air very easily, and for this reason it is used for drying gases.

Metaphosphoric acid (HPO_3) is obtained when phosphorus pentoxide absorbs moisture from the air, while if the same oxide is added to water and boiled, orthophosphoric acid (H_3PO_4) is formed. Both these acids give rise to series of salts known respectively as metaphosphates and orthophosphates. Phosphorus trioxide also reacts with water to form an acid – phosphorous acid (H_3PO_3).

A large percentage of the output of phosphorus is used in the manufacture of orthophosphoric acid. The conversion is carried out in two stages – the phosphorus is burned in air to obtain phosphorus pentoxide which then reacts with water. Much of the acid is, in turn, converted to phosphates. These are incorporated in large quantities in synthetic detergent powders to improve their dirt-suspended properties.

A great deal of the phosphate rock that is mined is not used to make phosphorus, but is treated with sulphuric acid to make 'superphosphate'.

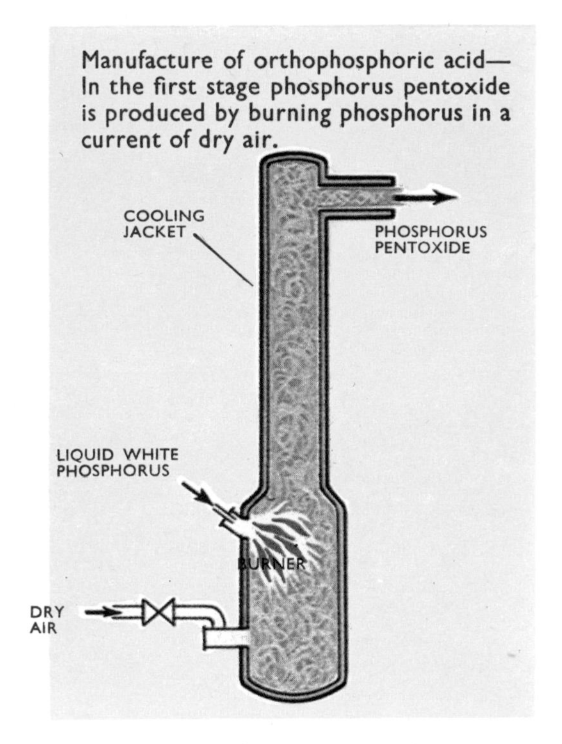

Manufacture of orthophosphoric acid—In the first stage phosphorus pentoxide is produced by burning phosphorus in a current of dry air.

This is an important fertilizer.

Phosphates are important in plant and animal cells since energy is stored in them and is released in reactions with these compounds. This stored energy is available to assist in the chemical processes going on within the living cells. Calcium phosphate is an important constituent of bones and teeth.

White phosphorus was formerly much used in matches. However, on account of its poisonous nature the manufacture of matches containing the white allotrope has long been forbidden by law. Red phosphorus has taken its place It is incorporated in the striking surface on the sides of boxes of safety matches. The heads of these matches contain a mixture of potassium chlorate (an oxidizing agent) and sulphur. They also contain other materials to control the chemical reaction which takes place once the match has been struck.

CHAPTER NINE

Group 6

Sulphur

The chief use of sulphur is in the manufacture of sulphuric acid which has enormous industrial importance. Sulphur is also used to dust hops and vines to kill off fungi which are parasitic and feed on these plants. Natural rubber is not very hard and resistant to wear. To make it suitable for use as car tyres it is vulcanized – a hardening treatment involving the use of sulphur. Sulphur is also used in the manufacture of gunpowder, match heads, and many drugs.

Sulphur is found near active or extinct volcanoes. In all regions where sulphur is found there has at some time been volcanic activity. Sulphur is a mild antiseptic and this yellow solid has been mined for centuries for its medicinal properties. It occurs naturally as the element sulphur in the volcanic regions of Italy and Sicily where it is found in a rocky earth, a mixture of sulphur, limestone and a mineral called gypsum.

Sulphur is one of the few elements that will burn readily. It burns with a pale blue flame and a choking nasty smell which is characteristic of sulphur dioxide, the gas formed as the result of the burning.

The age-old method of extracting the sulphur from the Earth is still used today, with certain modifications to make the process more efficient. A large heap of crude sulphur is built up on sloping ground and then set alight. The heat given out by the burning sulphur is sufficient to melt more sulphur which runs out of the fire and solidifies further down the slope. This wasteful process can burn as much as one-third of the sulphur. The solid lumps of sulphur can be broken up and sold under the name of *roll sulphur*. The solid lumps can also be purified by heating the sulphur without allowing it to catch fire and then collecting and cooling the sulphur gas which comes off. The impurities are left behind and the sulphur is now a yellow powder which is sold as *flowers of sulphur*. Enormous sulphur deposits have been discovered in Louisiana and Texas. In Louisiana the sulphur, which is almost pure, lies beneath a soggy layer of quicksand which is saturated with poisonous gases. This layer makes it impossible to mine the sulphur in the traditional manner. It is therefore extracted by the *Frasch process*. Water is heated under pressure to well over its normal boiling point so that its temperature rises to between 170 and 180 degrees centigrade. Still under pressure, it is forced down a pipe to melt the sulphur. Hot compressed air, too, is forced down to mingle with the molten sulphur and push it up through a third pipe to the surface where it emerges as a froth. The froth solidifies in large vats. This sulphur is over 95% pure and for most purposes needs no further purification. For convenience, so that there need be only

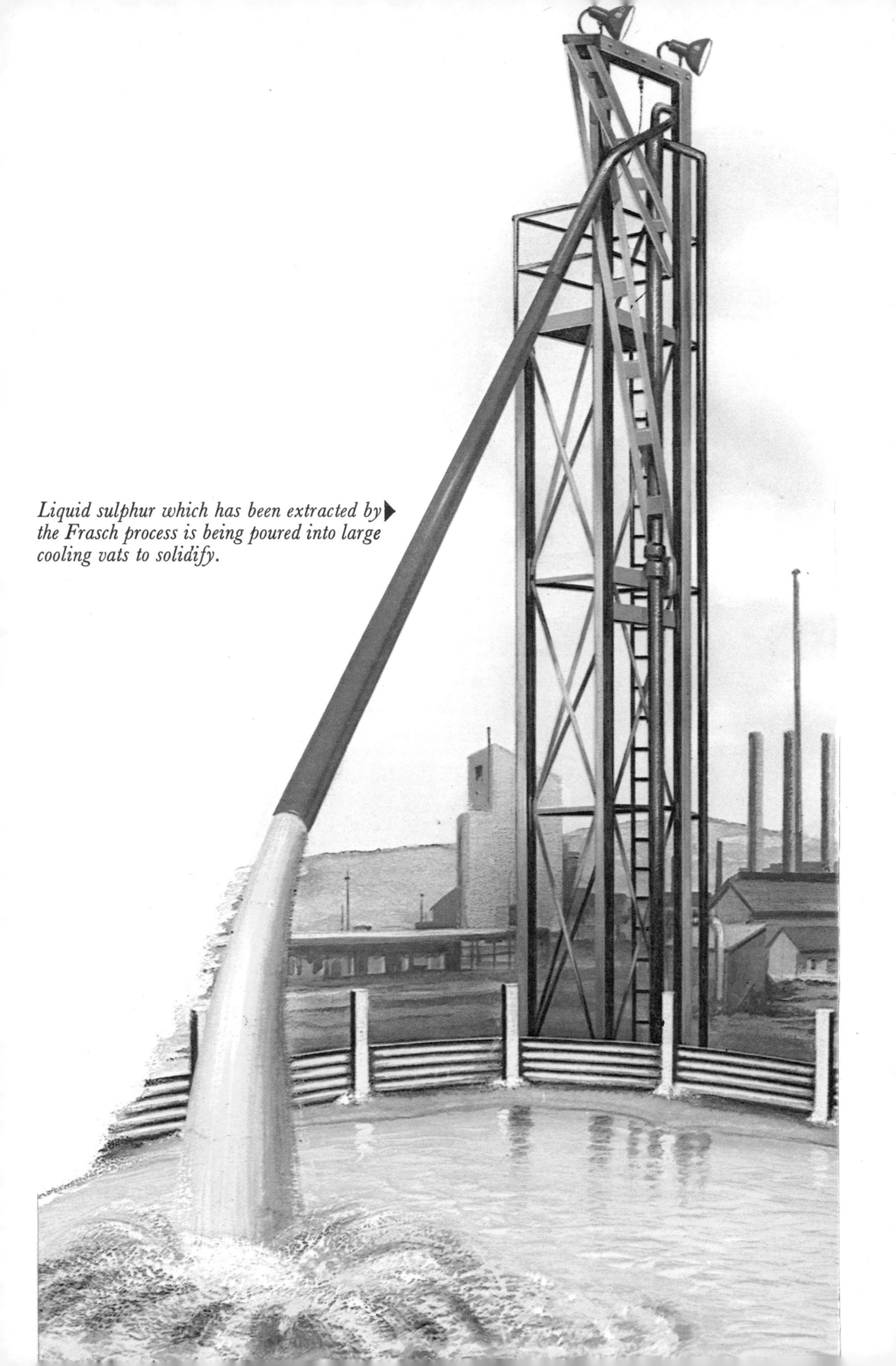

Liquid sulphur which has been extracted by the Frasch process is being poured into large cooling vats to solidify.

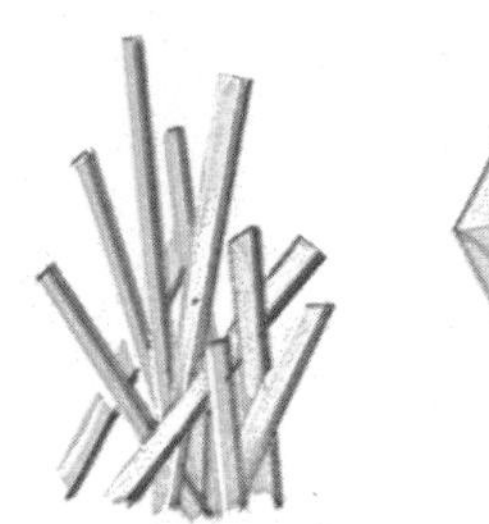
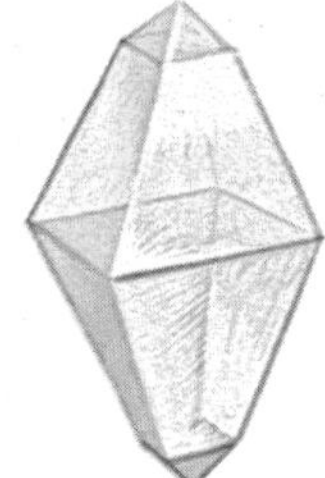

(Above) *Crystals of monoclinic sulphur.* (Right) *Crystal of rhombic sulphur.*

one borehole down to the sulphur, the three pipes are arranged one inside the other with the hot-air pipe in the middle and the hot-water pipe on the outside surrounding the exit pipe and keeping it warm (so that the sulphur is kept molten).

Most substances will form only one type of crystal, but sulphur will form several types. Because it can have several different crystalline forms it is said to be *allotropic.* At room temperature the rhombic-shaped sulphur crystals are stable and all other types of sulphur crystal will gradually change into the rhombic variety. Crystals of rhombic sulphur can be grown by dissolving some powdered roll sulphur in carbon disulphide (a strong smelling and inflammable liquid), filtering and allowing the solution to evaporate. The other well-known allotrope of sulphur is *prismatic* (or *monoclinic*) *sulphur*, so called because of its needle-like crystals. It can be made by melting sulphur and letting it cool until a crust forms on top. The crust is then punctured and the remaining liquid is poured away, leaving the needles of prismatic sulphur inside attached to the crust. These needles gradually change into rhombic sulphur. Another interesting form of sulphur is *plastic sulphur*, a stretchy elastic-like substance which can be made by pouring boiling sulphur into cold water. Because it hardens after a few hours, its elasticity cannot be put to any use.

The colour changes when sulphur is heated are interesting. Cold sulphur is a lemon-yellow solid. It melts to a thin clear amber-coloured liquid which darkens to a thick brown liquid which blackens and becomes more runny on further heating before it changes into a reddish-brown vapour.

Of the many compounds which contain sulphur, sulphuric acid is probably the best known. It has valuable uses in industry. The *sulphates* are salts derived from sulphuric acid. The sulphate which occurs most commonly in Nature is calcium sulphate, gypsum. Plaster of Paris is calcium sulphate and is made by heating gypsum to drive off the water attached to its molecules. Most cells of plants and animals contain a trace of sulphur in their proteins. Garlic and horseradish owe their strong taste to their sulphur compounds. When an egg goes bad a very unpleasant smell is given off. This is due to the gas hydrogen sulphide produced by the decaying protein. This gas has great use in the laboratory in analysis and so is in constant production there, often giving the laboratory a nasty smell.

Sulphur dioxide, the gas formed by the burning of sulphur, is used as a bleach for delicate materials. Its smell is none too sweet either. The whole range of sulphonamide drugs are compounds containing sulphur.

The Final Families

CHAPTER TEN

Group 7

The Halogens

The *halogens* are a family of *elements* which are very useful (both when free and when combined). *Fluorine* is a dangerous pale yellow gas which can be made into hydrofluoric acid, a substance used in industry for etching glass. *Bromine* is a red liquid which combines with silver to form silver bromide – the light-sensitive chemical put into films and photographic plates. *Iodine* is a black solid which gives a beautiful purple vapour on heating. It dissolves in alcohol to give "tincture of iodine", a brown liquid used as an antiseptic. *Chlorine* is an unpleasant pale green gas which was used in World War I as a poison gas. Small quantities of the gas in the air produce headaches and sore throats and sore eyes, whereas larger amounts will kill. Yet it is a remarkable fact that common salt contains chlorine, but in this chemically combined form it is not harmful, but beneficial.

These four *elements*, fluorine, chlorine, bromine and iodine, belong to the halogen family and are very much alike in their chemical behaviour.

The halogen family serves as an excellent demonstration of the way the periodic classification works. All of the members – fluorine, chlorine, bromine, and iodine – are oxidising agents and take part in substitution and addition reactions. As the members of the family become heavier and heavier, however, the reactivity is not so great. Fluorine is thus a stronger oxidising agent than chlorine, for example, and chlorine a stronger oxidising agent than bromine.

The physical properties are likewise similar, with the boiling and melting points increasing with an increase of the atomic weight.

The halogens are so extremely reactive chemically that they are not found free in nature. Free chlorine, being a gas, would otherwise be present in the air and life would be very unpleasant for us, if not impossible.

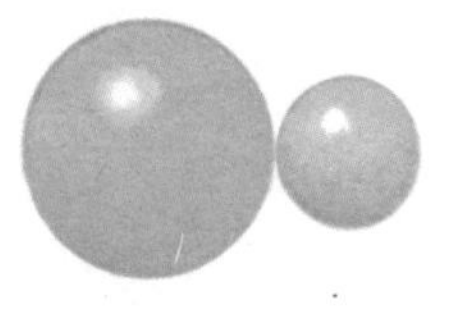

SODIUM CHLORIDE

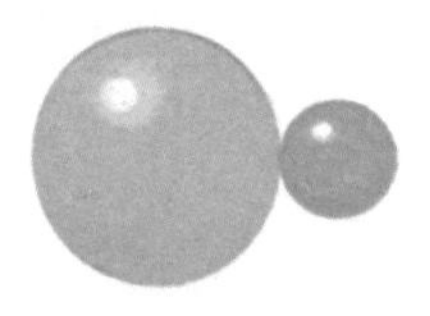

SODIUM FLUORIDE

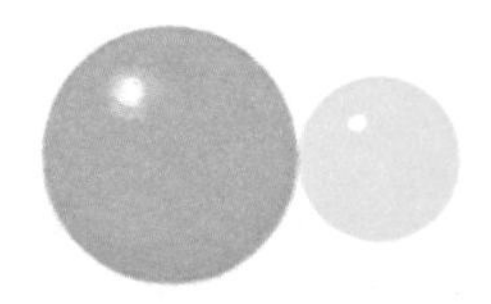

SODIUM BROMIDE

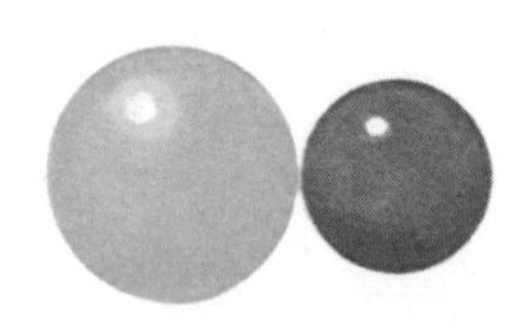

SODIUM IODIDE

The halogens do not occur as the free elements. Salts in which halogens are combined with metals are called halides. Those shown above are present in sea water.

It should be remembered, for more advanced studies, that in these halides the sodium metal is an 'ion', really smaller than the halogen to which it is joined.

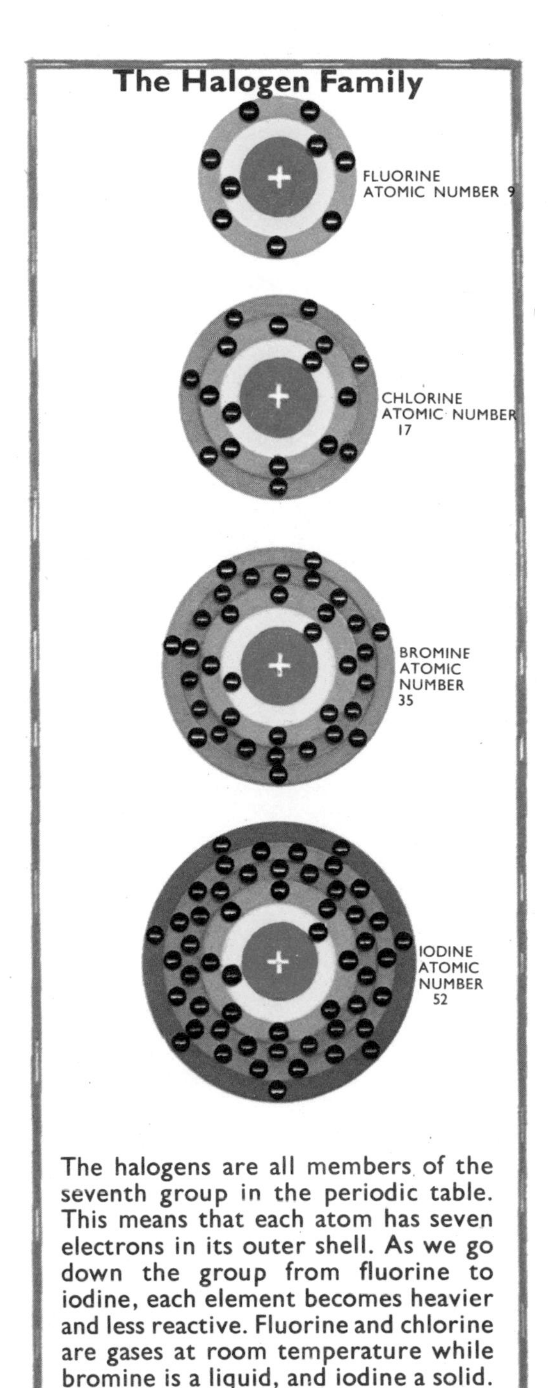

The halogens are all members of the seventh group in the periodic table. This means that each atom has seven electrons in its outer shell. As we go down the group from fluorine to iodine, each element becomes heavier and less reactive. Fluorine and chlorine are gases at room temperature while bromine is a liquid, and iodine a solid.

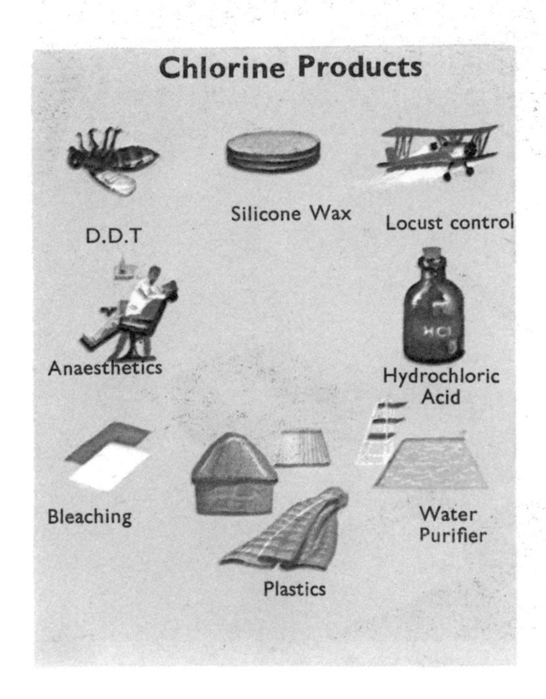

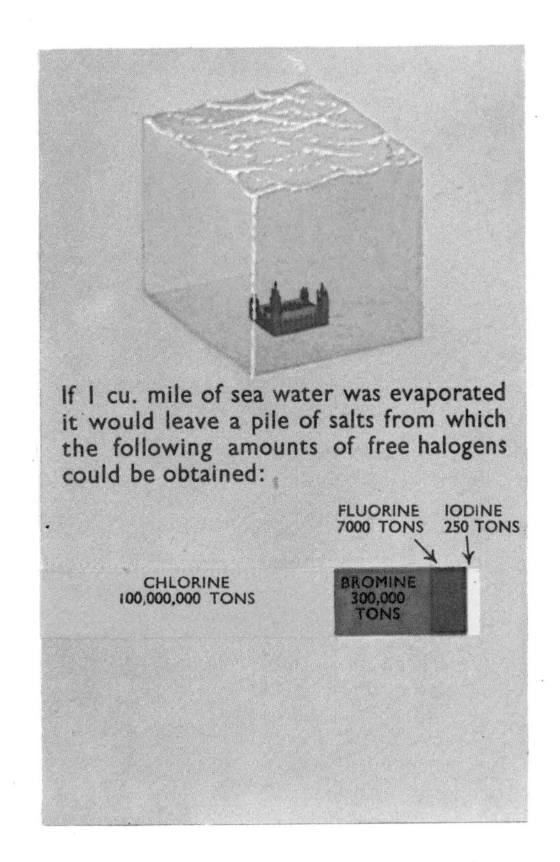

If I cu. mile of sea water was evaporated it would leave a pile of salts from which the following amounts of free halogens could be obtained:

Silver bromide in an emulsion of gelatine covers the surface of photographic films. It is sensitive to light, breaking down to metallic silver when exposed.

Each halogen has a similar electronic structure in that their atoms each have seven electrons in their outer shells, and there is a great tendency for them to gain an extra electron so making a stable shell of eight electrons. During chemical combination this state of stability is achieved, a single electron being gained from, say, metal atoms which tend to shed electrons. Thus the halogens are always combined very firmly with some other element or elements. It is possible, however, to split such combinations and release the free halogen. It is then necessary to store it carefully, otherwise it would quickly react with other substances and become recombined.

Fluorine

Fluorine combines vigorously with a great many other elements and compounds including most of those used for making chemical apparatus. Reactions involving fluorine and its compounds must be carried out in specially constructed vessels.

Hydrofluoric acid (HF) has been used for etching glass since 1670 but it was more than two hundred years later, in 1886, that a French chemist, Henri Moissan (1852–1907), succeeded in isolating fluorine. He added potassium hydrogen fluoride to the pure anhydrous acid and was then able to pass an electric current through the solution. By carrying out the electrolysis in a U-tube made of platinum-indium alloy with electrodes of the same material, Moissan obtained fluorine gas.

For many years after it was first isolated, fluorine was regarded as a chemical curiosity. However, in recent years a number of valuable uses have been found for it. For instance, sulphur hexafluoride (SF_6), prepared directly by the action of fluorine on sulphur, is used as an insulator in high voltage work. Hydrofluoric acid makes other important compounds. These include several compounds known as *freons*, such as dichloro-difluoromethane, CCl_2F_2, which are used as refrigerants and propellants in aerosol sprays. The plastic PTFE (polytetrafluoroethylene) is also made from hydrofluoric acid. It is especially useful as it is very resistant to chemical attack.

Fluorine is very corrosive and will cause severe burns if it comes into contact with the skin. Fluoride ions are poisonous if taken in quantity but in trace amounts (not more than one part in a million) they protect teeth against decay. Some water authorities now add minute amounts of fluoride to their water and some toothpaste manufacturers add fluorides to their products. Too much fluoride, apart from being harmful, discolours the teeth.

The Properties of Fluorine and its Compounds

There are marked differences between the behaviour of fluorine and its compounds, and of the other halogens and their compounds. For instance, silver fluoride is very soluble in water but the chloride, bromide and iodide of silver are all virtually insoluble.

Fluorine is a light yellow gas with a bitterly pungent smell. At −188°C it condenses into a pale yellow liquid. It is very reactive and, even at very low temperatures, it combines explosively with hydrogen. Fluorine reacts vigorously with phosphorus and liberates chlorine from potassium chloride in a displacement reaction:

$$F_2 + 2KCl \rightarrow 2KF + Cl_2$$

Many metals combine directly with fluorine and even the inert gases krypton and xenon form compounds with fluorine. Xenon, for example, combines with fluorine at 400°C to give xenon tetrafluoride, XeF_4.

Hydrofluoric acid is prepared by the action of concentrated sulphuric acid on fluorspar (calcium fluoride) which is one of the principal fluorine-containing minerals. Unlike the hydrides of the other halogens which are gases at room temperature, hydrofluoric acid is a liquid (boiling point 19·5°C). This is due to the existence of hydrogen bonds linking the various molecules to one another. For the same reason water is a liquid (not a gas like its near neighbour, hydrogen sulphide).

Metallic fluorides, which correspond in some respects with the chlorides, are formed by the action of hydrofluoric acid on metals or their oxides. However, there is an important difference between fluorides and chlorides in that acid fluorides (e.g. potassium hydrogen fluoride, KHF_2), are formed if the acid is present in excess.

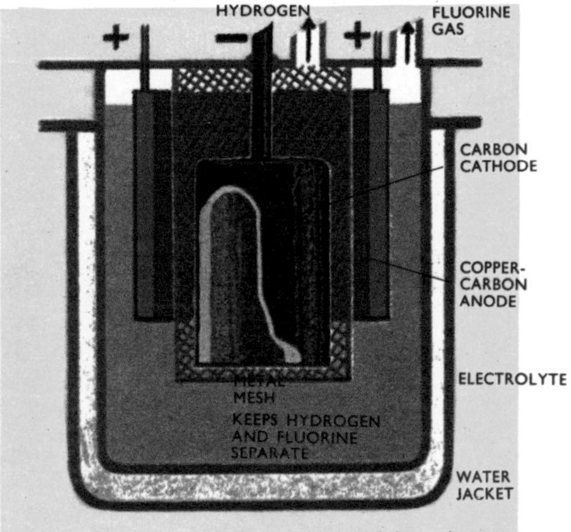

Fluorine gas can be prepared by electrolysing a fused mixture of composition KF.2HF. A heavy current is passed between electrodes of carbon and copper impregnated with carbon. Water is circulated in the water jacket to remove the heat generated by the passage of the heavy current.

Chlorine, the yellow-green poisonous gas, is found mainly in combination with sodium as common salt (sodium chloride, NaCl). It is washed out of rocks and carried down to the seas by rivers, where it forms more than 3% of the ocean's weight. It is found in some parts of the world in *salt beds* (old dried-up seas) which are sometimes 200 feet in thickness. From these, sodium chloride is quarried in the form of *rock salt*. Chlorine gas, on its own, is never found in nature – it is far too reactive.

Chlorine gas, when thoroughly dried and purified, is not very reactive but in the presence of small traces of water (always there when the gas is prepared in the laboratory or in industry) it becomes very active. A large range of chemical substances combines very readily with it – for example sulphur, arsenic and phosphorus all burn vigorously in chlorine, and in the presence of strong light, hydrogen and chlorine combine explosively. Chlorine gas also combines with zinc and iron to form chlorides when heat is applied, but will attack other metals only in the presence of traces of moisture. It liquefies at about – 34°C to a dark green liquid.

Apart from its appearance and pungent odour a test for chlorine gas is to see whether moist red litmus paper is bleached by the gas. The gas itself does not act as a bleach because the dry gas does not affect a piece of

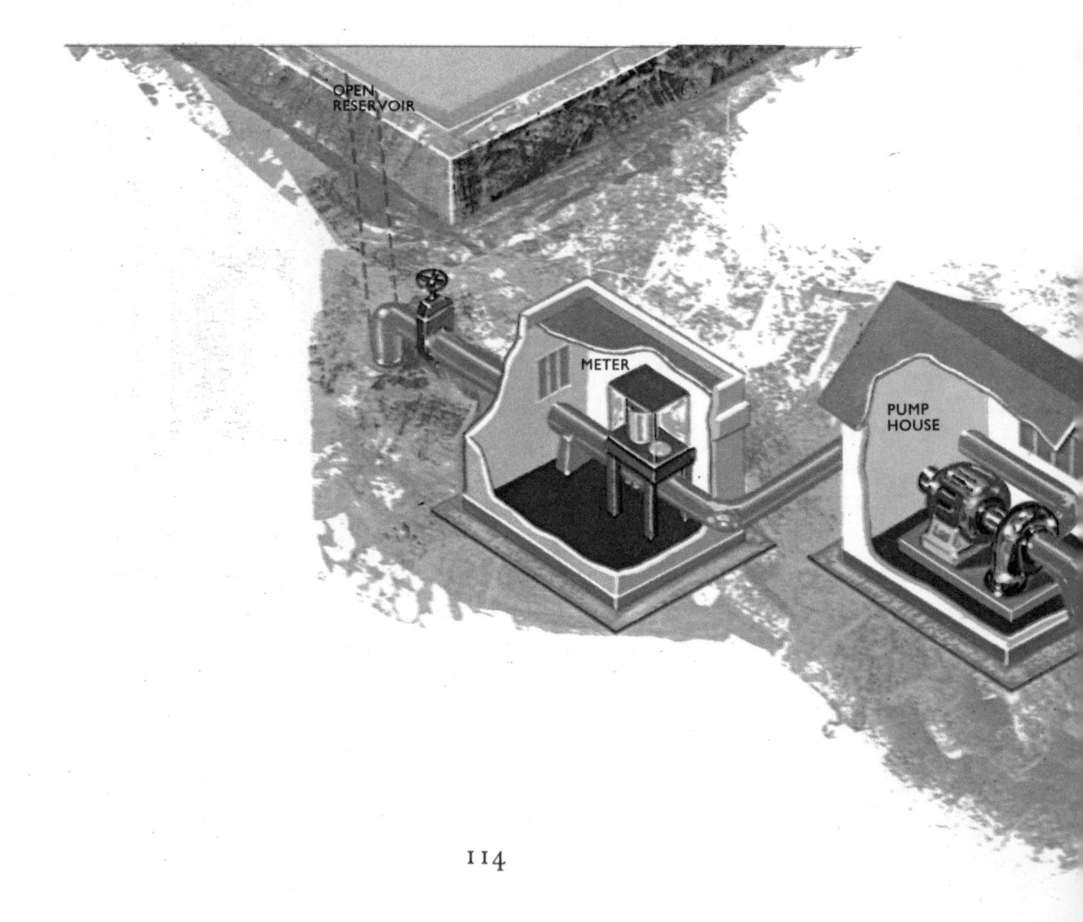

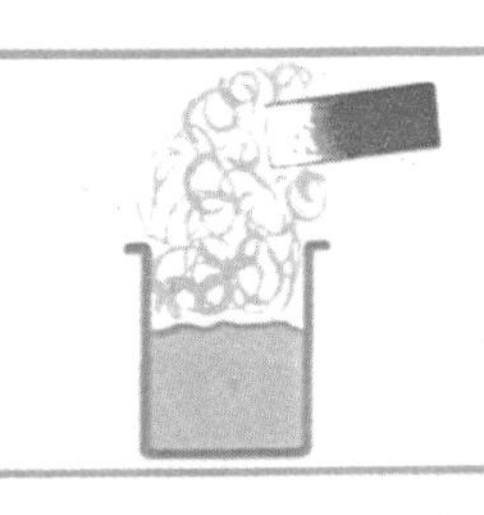

Chlorine in the presence of moisture acts as bleach. It is identified by its action on moist red litmus paper, which it bleaches white.

dry litmus paper. The bleaching action is caused by formation of hypochlorous acid (HOCl) when chlorine is dissolved in water:

$$Cl_2 + H_2O \rightleftarrows HCl + HOCl$$

When combined with oxygen, the chlorine atom forms a hypochlorite ion (OCl^-) that seems to possess bleaching properties. Thus, the formula of *bleaching powder* is often represented by $Ca(OCl)_2$, although the true structure is rather more complicated than this.

Addition and Substitution of Chlorine

Two important properties of chlorine are the ability to take part in *addition* and *substitution* reactions. In the addition reaction an unsaturated compound – one that can accept additional atoms to use all the available valency bonds – takes in the chlorine atom. Chlorine, like all the halogens, can be accepted in this way because it needs an additional electron to make up a full quota of eight electrons in its outer electron shell, and the atoms in the unsaturated compounds can provide them.

Addition reactions take place with both inorganic and organic unsaturated compounds. For example, carbon and oxygen are held together in carbon monoxide by an unsaturated bond which can be broken into by chlorine to form the saturated compound, phosgene:

$$CO + Cl_2 \rightarrow COCl_2$$

The unsaturated organic compound ethylene is saturated by chlorine to form ethylene dichloride:

$$C_2H_4 + Cl_2 \rightarrow C_2H_4Cl_2$$

In substitution reactions, chlorine atoms show the ability to push out other atoms and take their places in saturated compounds. For example, it displaces hydrogen from both ammonia and methane to form nitrogen trichloride and carbon tetrachloride:

$$NH_3 + 3Cl_2 \rightarrow 3HCl + NCl_3$$
$$CH_4 + 4Cl_2 \rightarrow 4HCl + CCl_4$$

Chlorination of water is used to kill off undesirable bacteria in the public water supply. The water from the reservoir is passed from filter units to the chlorination plant, where carefully controlled amounts of chlorine gas are applied.

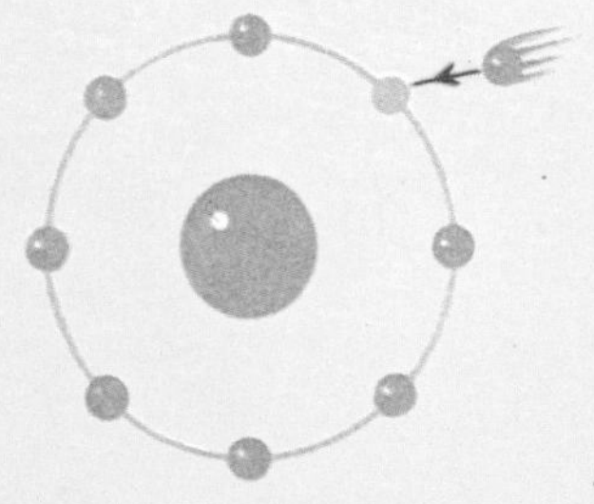

The chlorine atom has 7 electrons in its outer shell, and most of its chemical reactions result in it achieving a full shell of 8 electrons, needed to make it unreactive.

ADDITION

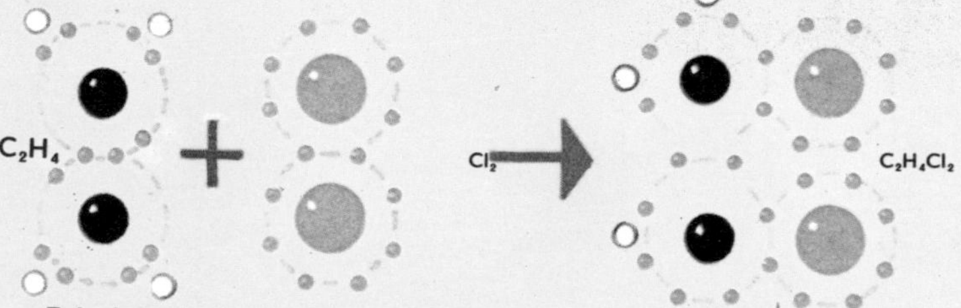

Ethylene has a double unsaturated bond joining the two carbon atoms, so there are two 'spare' electrons available. These are given to two chlorine atoms to make up complete shells of eight electrons in them, so ethylene dichloride is formed.

SUBSTITUTION

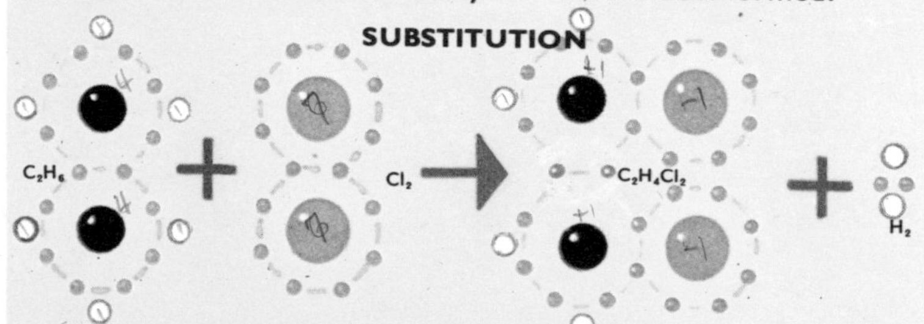

Chlorine atoms can replace other atoms in a substitution reaction. It can displace hydrogen atoms from the fully saturated compound ethane.

OXIDATION

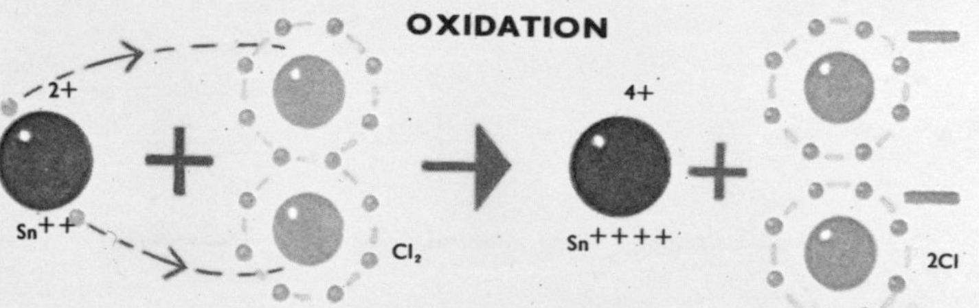

Chlorine is a very powerful oxidizing agent. If passed into solution of stannous chloride, the stannous (Sn^{++}) ions are oxidized to become stannic (Sn^{++++}) ions, the chlorine atom 'stealing' electrons from the stannous ions.

These reactions normally take place in a number of stages and in fact the partly substituted chloride of methane, $CHCl_3$, is the well-known compound, chloroform.

Chlorine as an Oxidising Agent

Another important chemical property of chlorine is that it can act as a powerful oxidising agent. It should be remembered that a proper definition of oxidation is not necessarily concerned with oxygen but with the loss of electrons from the atom. For example, when chlorine is passed into stannous chloride solution the stannous ions are oxidized to become stannic ions:

$$SnCl_2 + Cl_2 \rightarrow SnCl_4$$

or $$Sn^{2+} + Cl_2 \rightarrow Sn^{4+} + 2Cl^-$$

Once again, this is an example of chlorine atoms, short of a single electron to make up the 'magic number' of eight in the outer shell, 'stealing' a single electron from another atom.

Compounds of Chlorine

Chlorine, in combination with other elements, gives rise to a series of compounds called *chlorides*. The gas hydrogen chloride (HCl) dissolves in water to form hydrochloric acid, a most important chemical reagent. The family of metallic chlorides is formed by the action of hydrochloric acid on the metals themselves. For

Chlorine is produced in the cell by the electrolytic method. When a current is passed in the brine chloride ions pass to the graphite anode and chlorine gas is given off. Sodium ions pass to the mercury cathode where they form an amalgam. The amalgam is replaced by new mercury.

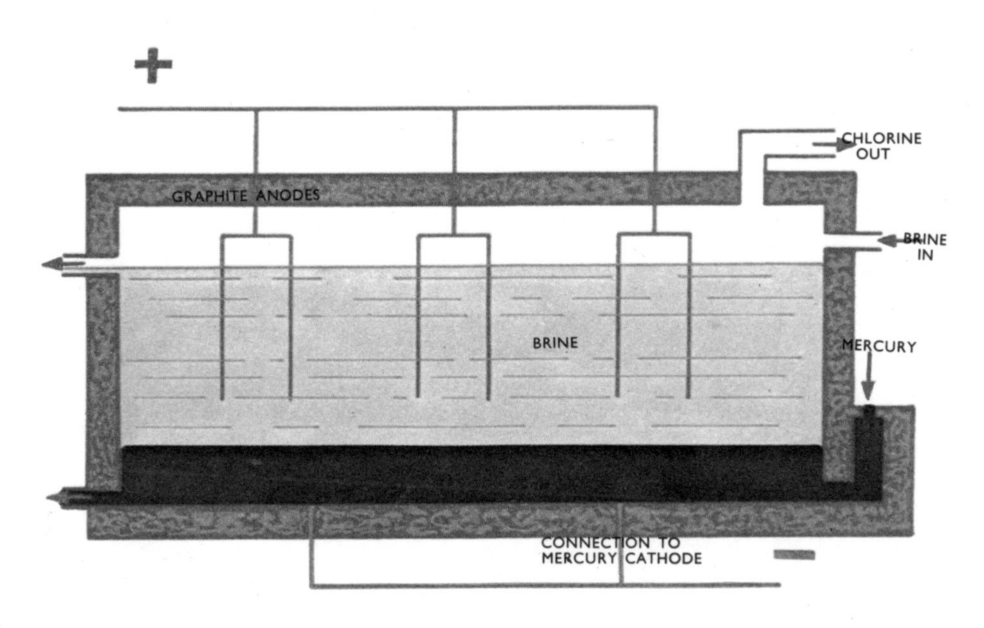

example, when the acid acts on metallic zinc, zinc chloride is formed:

$$Zn + 2HCl \rightarrow H_2 + ZnCl_2$$

Chlorides are also formed by the action of hydrochloric acid on metallic oxides. Then, water is liberated instead of hydrogen.

Chlorine also combines with oxygen to form a series of oxides – dichlorine monoxide Cl_2O, chlorine dioxide ClO_2, chlorine trioxide ClO_3, and dichlorine heptoxide, Cl_2O_7. When these oxides are dissolved in water they form a series of oxyacids – hypochlorous acid ($HOCl$), chlorous acid ($HClO_2$), chloric acid ($HClO_3$), and perchloric acid ($HClO_4$).

Preparation of Chlorine

In the laboratory, chlorine is prepared by the action of hydrochloric acid on manganese dioxide:

$$MnO_2 + 4HCl \rightarrow MnCl_2 + Cl_2 + 2H_2O$$

but chlorine is also released by the action of hydrochloric acid on either potassium permanganate or bleaching powder.

On the industrial scale, although chlorine was for many years produced by chemical means, electrical processes are now used.

In the *Kellner–Solvay* process a layer of mercury flows slowly over the bottom of a cell. The mercury forms a cathode and graphite anodes are suspended, in a brine solution, above the mercury. The sodium ions (Na^+) can travel to the mercury and form an amalgam with it. The sodium-mercury amalgam then flows into a water-filled vessel where the sodium attacks the water and forms soluble sodium hydroxide, whilst the pure mercury flows on. The chloride ions (Cl^-) are passed to the cathode where they lose their charge and form chlorine gas.

The Heavy Halogens

Like the other halogens the two heaviest common members of the family, bromine and iodine, are not found free in nature. They are much too reactive, the elements being strongly *electro-negative*. This means that bromine and iodine atoms are very eager to accept a single electron from the atoms of another element, and so are able to take part readily in chemical reactions. The heaviest halogen of all, astatine, is not found in nature at all. It is a comparatively short-lived radio-active element, formed when bismuth is bombarded with alpha particles.

Bromine

Bromine is a reddish-brown liquid that boils at 58·8°C to give off a dark brown vapour. It has a pungent odour and attacks the eyes and the throat, as well as the skin. It is found in sea-water and in natural salt deposits in

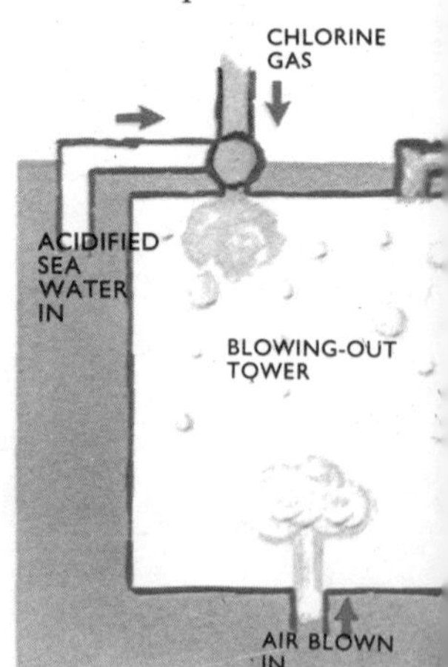

combination with sodium, calcium, potassium and magnesium. An important industrial method of preparation is to displace the bromine from the bromide ions present in sea water. Chlorine gas is blown through sea water, to which very small quantities of sulphuric acid have been added. The purpose of the acid is to stop the chlorine reacting with the water. Bromine is displaced, and is blown out by a current of air (see detailed diagram below).

This reaction provides an example of the greater chemical activity of the lighter members of the halogen family. Chlorine atoms are able to take away one electron each from each bromide ion, making chloride ions and bromine atoms:

$$Cl_2 + 2Br^- \rightarrow 2Cl^- + Br_2$$

Bromine is used in the manufacture of photographic film – silver bromide is a light-sensitive material, and the bromides of sodium and potassium are used as sleeping drugs. But the main use of bromine is to make ethylene dibromide ($C_2H_4Br_2$), used as an additive in motor spirit.

Iodine

'Iodine', as commonly known, is a brown liquid, used for dressing wounds. In fact, this is not pure iodine, but is a solution formed by dissolving the element in alcohol. The pure element itself is a black lustrous metallic-looking solid that melts at 113°C. At 187°C it boils to give off a deep violet-coloured vapour. It is found in small quantities in sea water and in sea plants, particularly sea weed, but the main source is the nitrate beds in Chile, where it is found in the form of sodium iodate, $NaIO_3$. Iodine is used in the manufacture of Polaroid film. It is an essential element in human diet, being required by the thyroid gland. For healthy growth small quantities of iodide salts must be present in food.

Although the iodine atom ranks as being highly reactive compared with many atoms of other elements, it is less reactive than the other common

Extraction of Bromine from Sea Water. Chlorine is passed into the acidified sea water and replaces bromine from the bromide salts. The bromine is blown out with an air blast and the bromine-laden air is mixed with sulphur dioxide. Hydrogen bromide is formed and this is mixed with chlorine which again releases bromine. This is steamed-out in the steaming-out tower and passes on to the condenser.

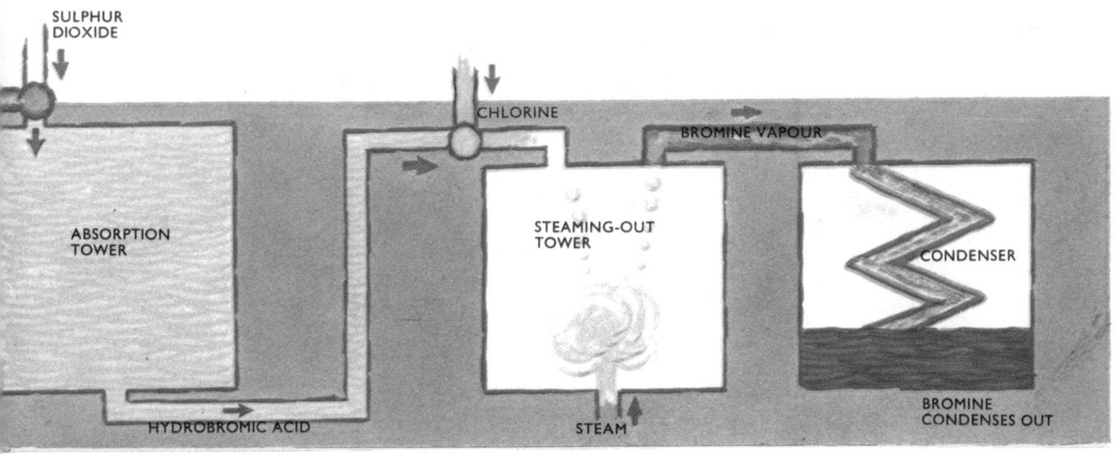

At normal temperatures pure iodine is a black metallic-looking solid. It can be detected in solution by the very sensitive starch test. Starch paper turns a deep blue in the presence of iodine.

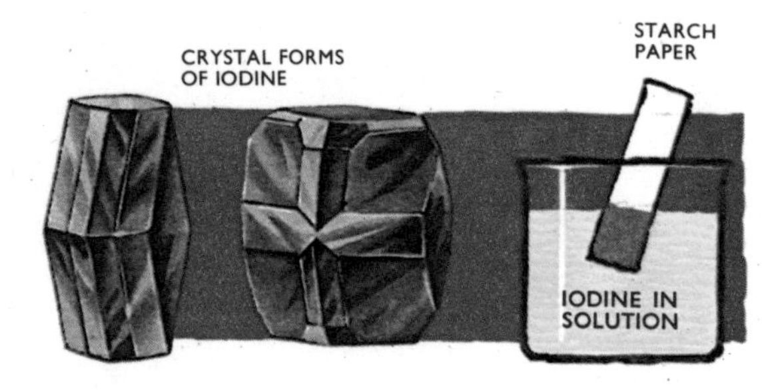

halogens. It is less electronegative than any of the other halogens and is a weaker oxidizing agent.

It is possible to get a good idea of the reactivity of a chemical substance by measuring the amount of heat given out when it reacts. When iodine combines with the metals it gives out less heat than the other halogens in similar reactions.

The Heaviest Halogen - Astatine

All the halogens have seven electrons in the outer shell of their atoms, and the heavier the atom, the less reactive it is. Their physical properties are graded with increase in mass. Fluorine, the lightest halogen, is a very reactive gas. Iodine is a near-metallic solid. Its atomic weight is 126·9 and it was thought that it was the heaviest existing halogen. Then, in 1940, the element astatine was discovered, and found to be a member of the halogen family. Its atomic weight is 211, and it is a short-lived radioactive element, whose properties are not yet fully known. However, it appears to resemble iodine in many ways, having an even more metallic appearance. Like iodine it can be taken up by the thyroid gland where the dangerous radiation it emits can destroy living tissue.

CHAPTER ELEVEN

Group 0

The Inert Gases

Helium, neon, argon, krypton, xenon and radon are the members of the family of elements called the inert gases. They are extremely unreactive. Helium, neon and argon are not at present known to form any compounds, and the others make only a limited number of compounds (see page 113). Whereas most other elements are found in Nature not on their own, but as compounds, these gases are always found as elements, i.e. never chemically combined with other substances. The atoms are, in fact, so 'anti-social' that they do not even join together in pairs as do the atoms of many elements such as oxygen and nitrogen.

Some atoms react because their normal structure is short of the 'ideal design' number of electrons, others because they have too many. They all want to become like inert gases with an 'ideal' outer shell. Because the inert gases have just the right number of electrons in their outer shell they are not inclined to do the extra work needed to make them combine.

Argon

Scientists have put this inactivity to good use. *Argon* at low pressure is used for filling electric-light bulbs. Electricity passes through a very fine filament made of the metal tungsten. The filament gets white hot and light is given out. If there were any oxygen present at this high temperature a chemical reaction would take place between the metal and the oxygen and the filament would turn into tungsten oxide which does not conduct electricity, and would flake off. In other words it would burn out. If argon is present then the filament is quite safe because inert argon will not react with it. If all the air was withdrawn from a bulb and it was not filled with any other gas, then the filament at this great temperature would boil off molecules from its surface, and by doing so would get thinner and wear out. So the argon does two jobs. It stops the filament from burning out when it is hot and it stops it from evaporating away.

Helium

Helium, because it is so unreactive, has taken the place of hydrogen for filling observation balloons. It is somewhat heavier than the extremely light hydrogen but it is the lightest

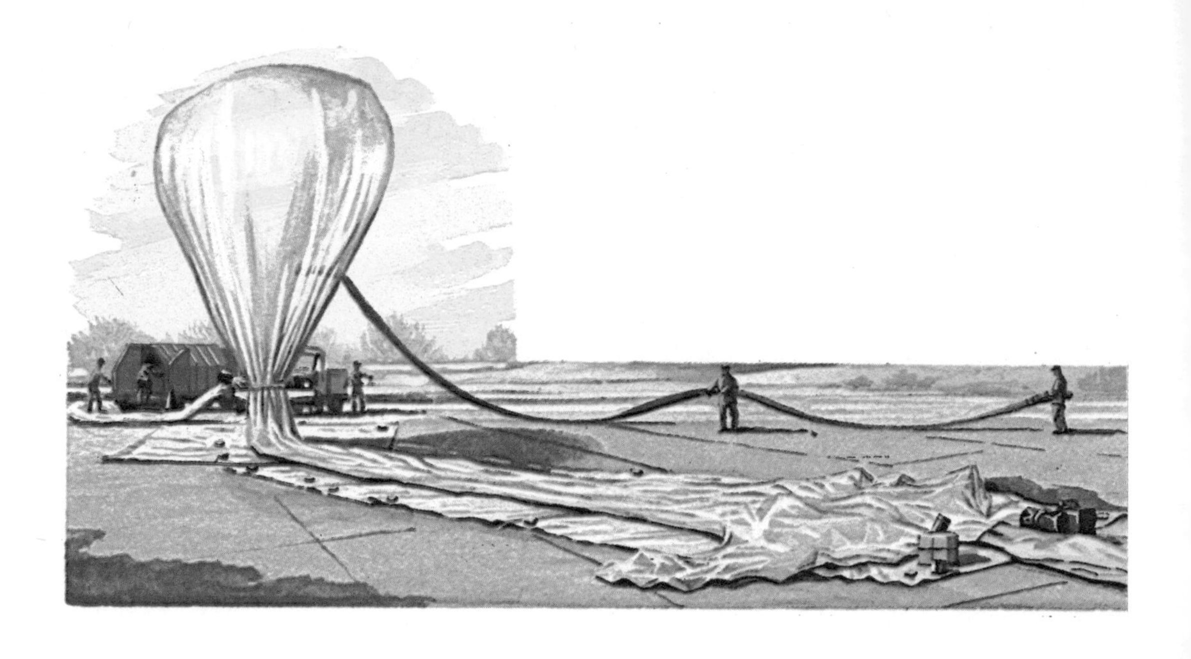

Filling a meteorological balloon with helium. Helium is, like hydrogen, very much lighter than an equal volume of air, hence its use in balloons and airships. Hydrogen proved to be a very dangerous substance to use in airships because it is so inflammable. But helium is one of the inert *gases. It does not burn at all.*

member of the inert gas family. Using it instead of hydrogen cuts out all danger of fire because helium cannot burn. Mixtures of helium and oxygen are nowadays breathed by deep-sea divers because, under high pressures, helium is less soluble in the bloodstream than nitrogen. This reduces the risk of 'diver's bends' which breathing ordinary air under pressure may produce.

Neon

An electric spark is passed through a tube of low pressure *neon.* The electrical energy enables the outer electrons of the neon atoms to skip a bit further away from their centres (nuclei) making the atom excited. Almost immediately the electrons skip back again, giving out their extra energy as orange light which is very brilliant, and has a high power of fog penetration. Neon lights are used in aerodrome beacons because they can be seen through fog. Pure neon can only make light of a reddish-orange colour. To make neon lights of other colours the glass tube is usually coated on the inside with a suitable powder or emulsion to give the colour required.

Krypton and Xenon

The photographer's flash tube, used for taking high speed pictures, is filled with a mixture of *krypton* and *xenon.* When a discharge (a spark of electricity) is passed through the tube, a very intense light suitable for photography is given out for a very short time. This flash apparatus can be used over and over again, unlike the flash bulbs which are used once and then thrown away.

Krypton is also used to fill the quartz-iodine bulbs used for very powerful car headlamps.

Radon

Radon, the heaviest member of the family, is a radioactive gas. The radiation it gives off is used in hospitals for treating some forms of cancer. The gas is made from radium salts and put into sealed tubes to be sent to the hospitals.

Helium, neon, argon, krypton and xenon are all naturally-occurring elements which are found in the atmosphere. Helium is also found in natural (oil-well) gas which can contain as much as 5% of it. Sometimes it is found dissolved in water. The inert gases, or rare gases, as they are sometimes called, are usually obtained by separating them from the air where together they make up rather less than 1% of its volume. Air is cooled sufficiently to make it become liquid, leaving the helium and neon behind as gases. As the liquid air is allowed to warm up the nitrogen boils off first, then argon, then oxygen, then krypton and finally xenon. The 'boiling off' takes place in a *fractionating column*—a piece of apparatus which separates the gases according to their different boiling points.

Chemical Elements—Symbols, atomic numbers and atomic weights

	Symbol	*Atomic Number*	*Atomic Weight*
Actinium	Ac	89	227·*
Aluminium	Al	13	26·97
Americium	Am	95	243·*
Antimony	Sb	51	121·76
Argon	A	18	39·944
Arsenic	As	33	74·91
Astatine	At	85	210·*
Barium	Ba	56	137·36
Berkelium	Bk	97	249·*
Beryllium	Be	4	9·013
Bismuth	Bi	83	209·00
Boron	B	5	10·82
Bromine	Br	35	79·916
Cadmium	Cd	48	112·41
Caesium	Cs	55	132·91
Calcium	Ca	20	40·08
Californium	Cf	98	251·*
Carbon	C	6	12·010
Cerium	Ce	58	140·13
Chlorine	Cl	17	35·457
Chromium	Cr	24	52·01
Cobalt	Co	27	58·94
Copper	Cu	29	63·54
Curium	Cm	96	247·*
Dysprosium	Dy	66	162·46
Einsteinium	Es	99	254·*
Erbium	Er	68	167·2
Europium	Eu	63	152·0
Fermium	Fm	100	253·*
Fluorine	F	9	19·00
Francium	Fr	87	223·*
Gadolinium	Gd	64	157·26
Gallium	Ga	31	69·72
Germanium	Ge	32	72·60
Gold	Au	79	197·2
Hafnium	Hf	72	178·6
Helium	He	2	4·003
Holmium	Ho	67	164·94
Hydrogen	H	1	1·0080
Indium	In	49	114·76
Iodine	I	53	126·92
Iridium	Ir	77	193·1
Iron	Fe	26	55·85
Krypton	Kr	36	83·80
Lanthanum	La	57	138·92
Lead	Pb	82	207·21
Lithium	Li	3	6·940
Lutetium	Lu	71	174·99
Magnesium	Mg	12	24·32

	Symbol	*Atomic Number*	*Atomic Weight*
Manganese	Mn	25	54·93
Mendelevium	Md	101	256·*
Mercury	Hg	80	200·61
Molybdenum	Mo	42	95·95
Neodymium	Nd	60	144·27
Neon	Ne	10	20·183
Neptunium	Np	93	237·*
Nickel	Ni	28	58·69
Niobium	Nb	41	92·91
Nitrogen	N	7	14·008
Nobelium	No	102	253·*
Osmium	Os	76	190·2
Oxygen	O	8	16·0000
Palladium	Pd	46	106·7
Phosphorus	P	15	30·98
Platinum	Pt	78	195·09
Plutonium	Pu	94	242·*
Polonium	Po	84	210·
Potassium	K	19	39·096
Praseodymium	Pr	59	140·92
Promethium	Pm	61	147·*
Protactinium	Pa	91	231·
Radium	Ra	88	226·05
Radon	Rn	86	222·
Rhenium	Re	75	186·31
Rhodium	Rh	45	102·91
Rubidium	Rb	37	85·48
Ruthenium	Ru	44	101·7
Samarium	Sm	62	150·43
Scandium	Sc	21	44·96
Selenium	Se	34	78·96
Silicon	Si	14	28·06
Silver	Ag	47	107·880
Sodium	Na	11	22·997
Strontium	Sr	38	87·63
Sulphur	S	16	32·066
Tantalum	Ta	73	180·88
Technetium	Tc	43	99·*
Tellurium	Te	52	127·61
Terbium	Tb	65	159·2
Thallium	Tl	81	204·39
Thorium	Th	90	232·12
Thulium	Tm	69	168·94
Tin	Sn	50	118·70
Titanium	Ti	22	47·90
Tungsten	W	74	183·86
Uranium	U	92	238·07
Vanadium	V	23	50·95
Xenon	Xe	54	131·3
Ytterbium	Yb	70	173·04
Yttrium	Y	39	88·92
Zinc	Zn	30	65·38
Zirconium	Zr	40	91·22

*The atomic weights of these radioactive elements depend upon the method of manufacture.

Index